National Institute on Alcohol Abus
Project MATCH Monograph Series
Volume 2

MOTIVATIONAL ENHANCEMENT THERAPY MANUAL

A Clinical Research Guide for Therapists Treating Individuals With Alcohol Abuse and Dependence

By:
William R. Miller, Ph.D.
Allen Zweben, D.S.W.
Carlo C. DiClemente, Ph.D.
Robert G. Rychtarik, Ph.D.

Project MATCH Monograph Series Editor:
Margaret E. Mattson, Ph.D.

U.S. Department of Health and Human Services
Public Health Service
National Institutes of Health

National Institute on Alcohol Abuse and Alcoholism
6000 Executive Boulevard
Rockville, Maryland 20892-7003

ECHO POINT BOOKS & MEDIA, LLC

Project MATCH is supported by grants under a cooperative agreement funded by the National Institute on Alcohol Abuse and Alcoholism (NIAAA) and implemented by nine clinical research units and a data coordinating center. The project was initiated and is administered by the Treatment Research Branch, NIAAA.

NIH Publication No. 94-3723
Reprinted 1999

Published by Echo Point Books & Media
Brattleboro, Vermont
www.EchoPointBooks.com

ISBN: 978-1-62654-857-2

Printed and bound in the United States of America

Acknowledgments

The overall effort to design all three manuals in this series and to implement the therapies in the Clinical Research Units was coordinated by the investigators at Yale University under the leadership of Drs. Kathleen Carroll and Bruce Rounsaville.

Project MATCH Research Group and Other Contributors

Principal and Coinvestigators ath the Sites

William Miller, Ph.D.
Reid Hester, Ph.D.
Center on Alcoholism, Substance Abuse and Addictions
University of New Mexico
Albuquerque, NM

Gerard Connors, Ph.D.
Robert Rychtarik, Ph.D.
Research Institute on Alcoholism
Buffalo, NY

Carrie Randall, Ph.D.
Raymond Anton, M.D.
Medical University of South Carolina and
Veterans Administration Medical Center
Charleston, SC

Ronald Kadden, Ph.D.
Ned Cooney, Ph.D.
University of Connecticut School of Medicine
Farmington, CT

Carlo DiClemente, Ph.D.
Joseph Carbonari, Ed.D.
University of Houston
Houston, TX

Allen Zweben, D.S.W.
University of Wisconsin-Milwaukee
Milwaukee, WI

Richard Longabaugh, Ed.D.
Robert Stout, Ph.D.
Brown University
Providence, RI

Dale Walker, M.D.
Dennis Donovan, Ph.D.
University of Washington and Seattle VA Medical Center
Seattle, WA

Coordinating Center Principal and Coinvestigators

Thomas Babor, Ph.D.
Frances Del Boca, Ph.D.
University of Connecticut
Farmington, CT

Kathleen Carroll, Ph.D.
Bruce Rounsaville, M.D.
Yale University
New Haven, CT

NIAAA Staff

John Allen, Ph.D.
Project Officer for Project MATCH
Chief, Treatment Research Branch

Margaret Mattson, Ph.D.
Staff Collaborator for Project MATCH

Cooperative Education Program

Lisa Marshall
Gallaudet University
Washington, DC

Consultants

Larry Muenz, Ph.D.
Gaithersburg, MD

Philip Wirtz, Ph.D.
George Washington University
Washington, DC

Contractor

Jane K. Myers
President
Janus Associates
Bethesda, MD

Foreword

A major focus of the efforts of the National Institute on Alcohol Abuse and Alcoholism (NIAAA) in treatment research is to rigorously test the patient-treatment matching approach to the clinical management of alcoholism. This commitment is particularly reflected in its multisite clinical trial, Project MATCH. This study is the first national, multisite trial of patient-treatment matching and one of the two largest current initiatives of NIAAA. Established under a cooperative agreement that allows direct collaboration between the Institute and the researcher, the project involves nine geographically representative clinical sites and a data coordinating center. Researchers in Project MATCH are among the most senior and experienced treatment scientists in the field. Both public and private treatment facilities, as well as hospital and university outpatient facilities, are represented.

The manuals in this series are the result of the collaborative efforts of the Project MATCH investigators and are used as guides by therapists in the trial. They are presented to the alcohol research community as standardized, well-documented intervention tools for alcoholism treatment research. The final reports of Project MATCH will inform us on the relative efficacy of the interventions being evaluated in the trial and on the types of clients who benefit the most from each of the therapies.

Until the final results from Project MATCH are presented to the community, these interim manuals summarize the consensus of the investigators on reasonable intervention approaches based on present knowledge. We look forward to offering further refinements of these approaches as Project MATCH data are analyzed and published and as the alcohol treatment field advances through the efforts of other ongoing research.

Enoch Gordis, M.D.
Director
National Institute on Alcohol Abuse
and Alcoholism

Preface

This manual for therapists is provided to the public to permit replication of the treatment procedures employed in Project MATCH, a multisite clinical trial of patient-treatment matching sponsored by the National Institute on Alcohol Abuse and Alcoholism (NIAAA). It describes Motivational Enhancement Therapy (MET), one of three treatment approaches studied in Project MATCH. Therapist manuals for the other treatments—Twelve-Step Facilitation Therapy (TSF) and Cognitive-Behavioral Coping Skills Therapy (CBT)—are available in volumes 1 and 3 of this series, respectively.

Rationale for Patient-Treatment Matching

Although a number of therapies have had varying degrees of success, no single treatment has been shown to be effective for all individuals diagnosed with alcohol abuse or dependence. In recent years, interest in the field has increasingly focused on patient-treatment matching to improve outcome. The hypothesis is that more beneficial results can be obtained if treatment is prescribed on the basis of individual patient needs and characteristics as opposed to treating all patients with the same diagnosis in the same manner.

Many investigators have turned their attention from main effects evaluations (i.e., studies that ask whether one intervention is more effective than another) to studies specifically designed to identify interactions between particular treatments and patient variables. While treatments may not appear to differ in effectiveness when applied to a heterogeneous client population, specific treatments may indeed be more or less effective for specific, clinically meaningful subgroups.

This reasoning has led to a new generation of alcoholism treatment research studies whose design is driven by the objective of finding effective "matches." Ultimately, the goal of this line of research is to provide the clinician with valid and practical rules applicable across a variety of treatment settings to assign patients to those treatment regimens particularly suited to them.

Project MATCH: An Overview

Project MATCH, a 5-year study, was initiated by the Treatment Research Branch of NIAAA in 1989. The details of the design and implementation of Project MATCH will be described in full in forthcoming publications. This section outlines the major features of the study.

The objective of Project MATCH is to determine if varying subgroups of alcohol abusing or dependent patients respond differentially to three treatments: (1) Twelve-Step Facilitation Therapy, (2) Cognitive-Behavioral Coping Skills Therapy, and (3) Motivational Enhancement Therapy. Each treatment is delivered during a 12-week period by trained therapists following a standardized protocol.

The project consists of two independent treatment-matching studies, one with clients recruited at five outpatient settings, the second with patients receiving aftercare treatment at four sites following an episode of standard inpatient treatment. Patients are randomly assigned to one of the three treatment approaches. Each study evaluates the interaction effects between selected patient characteristics and the three treatments.

Each of the nine study sites is recruiting approximately 150–200 clients. Clients are evaluated at intake and again at 3, 6, 9, 12, and 15 months. Outcome measures for the trial include drinking behavior, psychological and social function, and consequences of drinking Analyses of a priori hypotheses, as well as exploratory analyses, will show whether different patient characteristics are associated with differential treatment outcomes in each of the three therapeutic interventions.

Motivational Enhancement Therapy. MET is based on principles of motivational psychology and is designed to produce rapid, internally motivated change. This treatment strategy does not attempt to guide and train the client, step by step, through recovery, but instead employs motivational strategies to mobilize the client's own resources. MET consists of four carefully planned and individualized treatment sessions. The first two sessions focus on structured feedback from the initial assessment, future plans, and motivation for change. The final two sessions at the midpoint and end of treatment provide opportunities for the therapist to reinforce progress, encourage reassessment, and provide an objective perspective on the process of change.

The manual for this modality begins with an overview of MET and a description of the general principles to be applied. A special section discusses how to involve a significant other in MET. Then, specific guidelines are provided for how to structure the four MET sessions. Finally, recommendations are made for dealing with special problems that can arise in conducting MET. Appendix A offers specific instructions for preparing and explaining an individualized client feedback form. Copies of materials provided to MET clients are also included.

Appendix B offers guidelines for how to apply the manual—written from the perspective of outpatient treatment—within a program of aftercare following residential care.

Twelve-Step Facilitation Approach. This therapy is grounded in the concept of alcoholism as a spiritual and medical disease. The content of this intervention is consistent with the 12 Steps of Alcoholics Anonymous (AA), with primary emphasis given to Steps 1 through 5. In addition to abstinence from alcohol, a major goal of the treatment is to foster the patient's commitment to participation in AA. During the course of the program's 12 sessions, patients are actively encouraged to attend AA meetings and to maintain journals of their AA attendance and participation. Therapy sessions are highly structured, following a similar format each week that includes symptoms inquiry, review and reinforcement for AA participation, introduction and explication of the week's theme, and setting goals for AA participation for the next week. Material introduced during treatment sessions is complemented by reading assignments from AA literature.

Cognitive-Behavioral Coping Skills Therapy. This therapy is based on the principles of social learning theory and views drinking behavior as functionally related to major problems in the person's life. It posits that addressing this broad spectrum of problems will prove more effective than focusing on drinking alone. Emphasis is placed on overcoming skill deficits and increasing the person's ability to cope with high-risk situations that commonly precipitate relapse, including both interpersonal difficulties and intrapersonal discomfort, such as anger or depression. The program consists of 12 sessions with the goal of training the individual to use active behavioral or cognitive coping methods to deal with problems, rather than relying on alcohol as a maladaptive coping strategy. The skills also provide a means of obtaining social support critical to the maintenance of sobriety.

Caveats and Critical Considerations

Although all three manuals were developed for a randomized clinical trial focusing on patient-treatment matching hypotheses, the substance of the interventions is equally suitable for other research questions and designs. However, the reader needs to be aware of the parameters of Project MATCH.

Therapy is delivered in a structured research situation. All three treatments are manual guided and administered by experienced therapists who receive specialized training in one of the three project interventions. Therapists closely follow the procedures outlined in their manual, with regular supervision (by observation of videotapes) from both local and projectwide clinical supervisors.

This manual is written for therapists with similar intensive training and supervision. A summary of the procedures used to select, train, and supervise therapists in Project MATCH is provided in appendix C.

There is an important difference between a therapy textbook and a therapy manual. A therapy *textbook* is a comprehensive presentation of a particular therapeutic approach, usually describing a conceptual model, general principles, and a broad range of applications and examples. It is typically meant to facilitate broad utilization of a therapeutic approach by a wide range of practitioners in a variety of settings. A therapy *manual*, on the other hand, is intended to operationalize and standardize a treatment approach to be used in a particular context, usually a specific clinical trial. In writing a therapy manual, the authors must make a number of specific decisions (e.g., the number and timing of sessions, the content of each session) that are ordinarily left to clinical judgment in a therapy textbook.

This manual is designed to standardize MET as a four-session treatment modality within the particular context of Project MATCH. All treatments are preceded by the same extensive assessment battery, requiring approximately 7–8 hours. Abstinence is the expressed goal of all treatments, and except in unusual situations, all sessions are videotaped. Each treatment session is preceded by a breath test to ensure sobriety, and a positive breath alcohol reading results in rescheduling the session. Therapists are prohibited from mixing MET with other treatment approaches, and the purity of approach is maintained by local and national supervisors who review videotapes. All therapy has to be completed within 90 days. A significant other can be invited to participate in up to two sessions.

Other design requirements of clinical trials are likewise standardized across all sites, including features such as defined patient eligibility criteria, randomized assignment of treatment, and guidelines for dealing with patients who are late or absent for treatment sessions or who show significant clinical deterioration during the course of the intervention. Guidelines regulate and document the amount and type of therapy over and above that provided by Project MATCH that a client receives during the study. Data collection and delivery of treatment are kept strictly separate, with the former being handled by research assistants under the supervision of the project coordinators. The three manuals refer to these Project MATCH-specific procedures with the knowledge that some readers may wish to follow similar guidelines, while others may choose to devise new guidelines more appropriate to the requirements of their own project.

The therapist style and many specific concepts embodied in this manual were drawn from Miller and Rollnick's (1991) *Motivational Interviewing*. We are grateful to Guilford Press for their permission to publish this specific adaptation Similar approaches have been more briefly described elsewhere (Edwards and Orford 1977; Miller 1983; van Bilsen and van Ernst 1986; Zweben et al. 1983, 1988). The bibliography of this manual provides a range of clinical, videotape, and research resources for further reference.

The general therapeutic principles underlying MET can be applied in many other ways than those delineated here (Miller and Rolinick 1991). Under ordinary circumstances, the number, duration, and distribution of sessions could be flexible. Significant others might be involved in all sessions or none at all. The goals of therapy might be more flexible (Miller 1987), and motivational-counseling procedures could be intermixed with other therapeutic strategies. The specific prescriptions outlined in this manual are imposed for purposes of standardization and separation of treatments in Project MATCH.

The staffs of Project MATCH and NIAAA make no claims or guarantees regarding the effectiveness of the treatment procedures described in this manual. Although the principles of MET are well grounded in clinical and experimental research, the specific efficacy of MET as outlined in this manual remains to be tested. The final reports of Project MATCH will provide clearer information on the efficacy of this approach relative to others and on the types of clients for whom it may be optimal. In the interim, this manual offers a detailed description of MET procedures as constructed by consensus among the investigators and implemented by the therapists of Project MATCH. All manuals of this kind should be regarded as under development and subject to ongoing improvement based on subsequent research and experience.

The planning and operation of Project MATCH and the products now resulting from it, including this series of manuals, reflect the efforts of many individuals over a period of several years. Their dedication and collegial collaboration have been remarkable and will enrich the field of alcoholism treatment research for years to come.

> Margaret E. Mattson, Ph.D.
> Project MATCH Staff Collaborator
> Project MATCH Monograph Series Editor
> Division of Clinical and Prevention
>   Research
> National Institute on Alcohol Abuse and
>   Alcoholism

Contents

Introduction

Overview

Motivational Enhancement Therapy (MET) is a systematic intervention approach for evoking change in problem drinkers. It is based on principles of motivational psychology and is designed to produce rapid, internally motivated change. This treatment strategy does not attempt to guide and train the client, step by step, through recovery, but instead employs motivational strategies to mobilize the client's own change resources.

Treatment is preceded by an extensive assessment battery (appendix A) requiring approximately 7–8 hours. Each treatment session is preceded by a breath test to ensure sobriety, and a positive breath alcohol reading is cause for rescheduling the session.

As offered in Project MATCH, MET consists of four carefully planned and individualized treatment sessions. Whenever possible, the client's spouse or another "significant other" is included in the first two of these four sessions. The first treatment session (week 1) focuses on (1) providing structured feedback from the initial assessment regarding problems associated with drinking, level of consumption and related symptoms, decisional considerations, and future plans and (2) building client motivation to initiate or continue change. The second session (week 2) continues the motivation enhancement process, working toward consolidating commitment to change. In two followthrough sessions, at week 6 and week 12, the therapist continues to monitor and encourage progress. All therapy is completed within 90 days.

MET is not intended to be a minimal or control treatment condition. MET is, in its own right, an effective outpatient treatment strategy which, by virtue of its rationale and content, requires fewer therapist-directed sessions than some alternatives. It may, therefore, be particularly useful in situations where contact with problem drinkers is limited to few or infrequent sessions (e.g., in general medical practice or in employee assistance programs). Treatment outcome research strongly supports MET strategies as effective in producing change in problem drinkers.

The initial presentation of MET in this manual is written from the perspective of outpatient treatment. These procedures can also be

Research Basis for MET

applied in aftercare, however, and such adaptation is addressed in appendix B.

For more than two decades, research has pointed to surprisingly few differences in outcome between longer, more intensive alcohol treatment programs and shorter, less intensive, even relatively brief alternative approaches (Annis 1985; Miller and Hester 1986b; Miller and Rollnick 1991; U. S. Congress, Office of Technology Assessment 1983). One interpretation of such findings is that all alcohol treatments are equally ineffective. A larger review of the literature, however, does not support such pessimism. Significant differences among alcohol treatment modalities are found in nearly half of clinical trials, and relatively brief treatments have been shown in numerous studies to be more effective than no intervention (Holder et al. 1991).

An alternative interpretation of this outcome picture is that many treatments contain a common core of ingredients which evoke change and that additional components of more extensive approaches may be unnecessary in many cases. This has led, in the addictions field as elsewhere, to a search for the critical conditions that are necessary and sufficient to induce change (e.g., Orford 1986). Miller and Sanchez (in press) described six elements which they believed to be active ingredients of the relatively brief interventions that have been shown by research to induce change in problem drinkers, summarized by the acronym FRAMES:

- FEEDBACK of personal risk or impairment

- Emphasis on personal RESPONSIBILITY for change

- Clear ADVICE to change

- A MENU of alternative change options

- Therapist EMPATHY

- Facilitation of client SELF-EFFICACY or optimism

These therapeutic elements are consistent with a larger review of research on what motivates problem drinkers for change (Miller 1985; Miller and Rollnick 1991).

Therapeutic interventions containing some or all of these motivational elements have been demonstrated to be effective in initiating treatment and in reducing long-term alcohol use, alcohol-related problems, and health consequences of drinking. Table 1 summarizes this research. It is noteworthy that, in a number of these studies, the motivational

Table 1. Specific FRAMES components of evaluated brief interventions

Author	Feedback	Response	Advice	Menu	Empathy	Self-Efficacy	Outcome
*Anderson and Scott 1992	Yes	Yes	Yes	Yes	Yes	Yes	Brief > No counseling
*Babor and Grant 1991	Yes	Yes	Yes	Manual	Yes	Yes	Brief > No counseling
*Bien 1991	Yes	Yes	Yes	No	Yes	Yes	Brief > No counseling
*Brown and Miller 1992	Yes	Yes	Yes	No	Yes	Yes	Brief > No counseling
*Carpenter et al. 1985	Yes	No	Yes	No	No	No	Brief = Extended counseling
*Chapman and Huygens 1988	Yes	Yes	Yes	Yes	No	Yes	Brief = IPT = OPT treatment
*Chick et al. 1985	Yes	Yes	Yes	No	Yes	Yes	Brief > No counseling
*Chick et al. 1988	No	Yes	Yes	No	No	No	Brief < Extended motiv cnslg
Daniels et al. 1992	Yes	No	Yes	Manual	No	No	Advice + Manual = No advice
Drummond et al. 1992	Yes	No	Yes	No	No	No	Brief = OPT treatment
Edwards et al. 1977	Yes	Yes	Yes	No	Yes	Yes	Brief = OPT/IPT treatment
Elvy et al. 1988	Yes	No	Yes	No	No	No	Brief > No counseling
*Harris and Miller 1990	No	Yes	Yes	Manual	Yes	Yes	Brief = Extended > No treatment
*Heather et al. 1986	Yes	Yes	Manual	Manual	No	No	Manual > No manual
*Heather et al. 1987	Yes	Yes	Yes	Manual	No	No	Brief = No counseling
*Heather et al. 1990	Yes	Yes	Yes	Manual	No	No	Manual > No manual
*Kristenson et al. 1983	Yes	Yes	Yes	No	Yes	Yes	Brief > No counseling
Kuchipudi et al. 1990	Yes	No	Yes	Yes	No	No	Brief = No counseling
Maheswaran et al. 1990	Yes	No	Yes	No	No	No	Brief > No counseling
*Miller and Taylor 1980	No	Yes	Yes	Manual	Yes	Yes	Brief = Behavioral counseling
*Miller et al. 1980	No	Yes	Yes	Manual	Yes	Yes	Brief = Behavioral counseling
*Miller et al. 1981	No	Yes	Yes	Manual	Yes	Yes	Brief = Behavioral counseling
*Miller et al. 1988	Yes	Yes	Yes	Yes	Yes	Yes	Brief > No counseling
*Miller et al. 1991	Yes	Yes	Yes	Yes	Yes	Yes	Brief > No counseling
*Persson and Magnusson 1989	Yes	Yes	No	Yes	Yes	Yes	Brief > No counseling
*Robertson et al. 1986	Yes	Yes	Yes	Yes	Yes	Yes	Brief < Behavioral counseling
*Romelsjo et al. 1989	Yes	Yes	Yes	No	Yes	Yes	Brief = OPT treatment
*Sannibale 1989	Yes	Yes	Yes	No	Yes	Yes	Brief = OPT treatment
*Scott and Anderson 1990	Yes	Yes	Yes	Yes	Yes	Yes	Brief = No counseling
*Skutle and Berg 1987	No	Yes	Yes	Yes+ Man	Yes	Yes	Brief = Behavioral counseling
*Wallace et al. 1988	Yes	Yes	Yes	Manual	Yes	Yes	Brief > No counseling
*Zweben et al. 1988	Yes	Yes	Yes	Yes	No	Yes	Brief = Conjoint therapy
Percent Yes	81	81	100	59	63	69	

Source: Bien, Miller, and Tonigan 1992.
NOTE: Components listed are characteristics of the brief intervention in each study.
* Additional information obtained from the study's authors.
Manual = Manual-guided therapy; IPT = Inpatient treatment setting; OPT = Outpatient treatment setting

intervention yielded comparable outcomes even when compared with longer, more intensive alternative approaches.

Further evidence supports the efficacy of the therapeutic *style* that forms the core of MET. The therapist characteristic of "accurate empathy," as defined by Carl Rogers and his students (e.g., Rogers 1957, 1959; Truax and Carkhuff 1967), has been shown to be a powerful predictor of therapeutic success with problem drinkers, even when treatment is guided by another (e.g., behavioral) rationale (Miller et al. 1980; Valle 1981). Miller, Benefield, and Tonigan (in press) reported that the degree to which therapists engaged in direct confrontation (conceptually opposite to an empathic style) was predictive of continued client drinking 1 year after treatment.

Stages of Change

The MET approach is further grounded in research on processes of natural discovery. Prechovaska and DiClemente (1982, 1984, 1985, 1986) have described a transtheoretical model of how people change addictive behaviors, with or without formal treatment. In a transtheoretical perspective, individuals move through a series of stages of change as they progress in modifying problem behaviors. This concept of stages is important in understanding change. Each stage requires certain tasks to be accomplished and certain processes to be used in order to achieve change. Six separate stages were identified in this model (Prochaska and DiClemente 1984, 1986).

People who are not considering change in their problem behavior are described as PRECONTEMPLATORS. The CONTEMPLATION stage entails individuals' beginning to consider both that they have a problem and the feasibility and costs of changing that behavior. As individuals progress, they move on to the DETERMINATION stage, where the decision is made to take action and change. Once individuals begin to modify the problem behavior, they enter the ACTION stage, which normally continues for 3–6 months. After successfully negotiating the action stage, individuals move to MAINTENANCE or sustained change. If these efforts fail, a RELAPSE occurs, and the individual begins another cycle (see figure 1).

The ideal path is directly from one stage to the next until maintenance is achieved. For most people with serious problems related to drinking, however, the process involves several slips or relapses which represent failed action or maintenance. The good

Figure 1. A Stage Model of the Process of Change
Prochaska and DiClemente

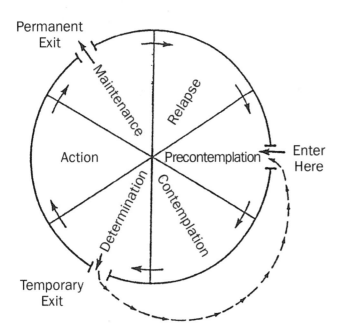

news is that most who relapse go through the cycle again and move back into contemplation and the change process. Several revolutions through this cycle of change are often needed to learn how to maintain change successfully.

From a stages-of-change perspective, the MET approach addresses where the client currently is in the cycle of change and assists the person to move through the stages toward successful sustained change. For the ME therapist, the contemplation and determination stages are most critical. The objective is to help clients seriously consider two basic issues. The first is how much of a problem their drinking behavior poses for them and how their drinking is affecting them (both positively and negatively). Tipping the balance of these pros and cons of drinking toward change is essential for movement from contemplation to determination. Second, the client in contemplation assesses the possibility and the costs/benefits of changing the problem behavior. Clients consider whether they will be able to make a change and how that change will affect their lives.

In the determination stage, clients develop a firm resolve to take action. That resolve is influenced by past experiences with change attempts. Individuals who have made unsuccessful attempts to change their drinking behavior in the past need encouragement to decide to go through the cycle again.

Understanding the cycle of change can help the ME therapist to empathize with the client and can give direction to intervention strategies. Though individuals move through the cycle of change in their own ways, it is the same cycle. The speed and efficiency of movement through the cycle, however, will vary. The task is to assist the individual in moving from one stage to the next as swiftly and effectively as possible.

In sum, MET is well grounded in theory and research on the successful resolution of alcohol problems. It is consistent with an understanding of the stages and processes that underlie change in addictive behaviors. It draws on motivational principles that have been derived from both experimental and clinical research. A summary of alcohol treatment outcome research reveals that a motivational approach of this kind is strongly supported by clinical trials: its overall effectiveness compares favorably with outcomes of alternative treatments, and when cost-effectiveness is considered, an MET strategy fares well indeed in comparison with other approaches (Holder et al. 1991).

Clinical Considerations

Rationale and Basic Principles

The MET approach begins with the assumption that the responsibility and capability for change lie within the client. The therapist's task is to create a set of conditions that will enhance the client's own motivation for and commitment to change. Rather than relying upon therapy sessions as the primary locus of change, the therapist seeks to mobilize the client's inner resources as well as those inherent in the client's natural helping relationships. MET seeks to support *intrinsic* motivation for change, which will lead the client to initiate, persist in, and comply with behavior change efforts. Miller and Rollnick (1991) have described five basic motivational principles underlying such an approach:

- Express empathy

- Develop discrepancy

- Avoid argumentation

- Roll with resistance

- Support self-efficacy

Express Empathy

The ME therapist seeks to communicate great respect for the client. Communications that imply a superior/inferior relationship between therapist and client are avoided. The therapist's role is a blend of supportive companion and knowledgeable consultant. The client's freedom of choice and self-direction are respected. Indeed, in this view, *only* the clients can decide to make a change in their drinking and carry out that choice. The therapist seeks ways to compliment rather than denigrate, to build up rather than tear down. Much of MET is *listening rather than telling*. Persuasion is gentle, subtle, always with the assumption that change is up to the client. The power of such gentle, nonaggressive persuasion has been widely recognized in clinical writings, including Bill Wilson's own advice to alcoholics on "working with others" (*Alcoholics Anonymous* 1976). Reflective listening (accurate empathy) is a key skill in motivational interviewing. It communicates an acceptance of clients as they are, while also supporting them in the process of change.

Develop Discrepancy

Motivation for change occurs when people *perceive a discrepancy between where they are and where they want to be.* The MET approach seeks to enhance and focus the client's attention on such discrepancies with regard to drinking behavior. In certain cases (e.g., the pre-contemplators in Prochaska and DiClemente's model), it may be necessary first to *develop* such discrepancy by raising clients' awareness of the personal consequences of their drinking. Such information, properly presented, can precipitate a crisis (critical mass) of motivation for change. As a result, the individual may be more willing to enter into a frank discussion of change options in order to reduce the perceived discrepancy and regain emotional equilibrium. When the client enters treatment in the later contemplation stage, it takes less time and effort to move the client along to the point of determination for change.

Avoid Argumentation

If handled poorly, ambivalence and discrepancy can resolve into defensive coping strategies that reduce the client's discomfort but do not alter drinking and related risks. An unrealistic (from the clients' perspective) attack on their drinking behavior tends to evoke defensiveness and opposition and suggests that the therapist does not really understand.

The MET style explicitly avoids direct argumentation, which tends to evoke resistance. No attempt is made to have the client accept or "admit" a diagnostic label. The therapist does not seek to prove or convince by force of argument. Instead, the therapist employs other strategies to assist the client to see accurately the consequences of drinking and to begin devaluing the perceived positive aspects of alcohol. When MET is conducted properly, *the client and not the therapist voices the arguments for change* (Miller and Rollnick 1991).

Roll With Resistance

How the therapist handles client "resistance" is a crucial and defining characteristic of the MET approach. MET strategies do not meet resistance head on, but rather "roll with" the momentum, with a goal of shifting client perceptions in the process. New ways of thinking about problems are invited but not imposed. Ambivalence is viewed as normal, not pathological, and is explored openly. *Solutions are usually evoked from the client rather than provided by the therapist.* This approach for dealing with resistance is described in more detail later.

Support Self-Efficacy

People who are persuaded that they have a serious problem will still not move toward change unless there is hope for success. Bandura (1982) has described "self-efficacy" as a critical determinant of behavior change. Self-efficacy is, in essence, the belief that one can perform a particular behavior or accomplish a particular task. In this case, clients must be persuaded that it is possible to change their own drinking and thereby reduce related problems. In everyday language, this might be called hope or optimism, though an overall optimistic nature is not crucial here. Rather, it is the clients' *specific belief that they can change the drinking problem.* Unless this element is present, a discrepancy crisis is likely to resolve into defensive coping (e.g., rationalization, denial) to reduce discomfort without changing behavior. This is a natural and understandable protective process. If one has little hope that things could change, there is little reason to face the problem.

Differences From Other Treatment Approaches

The MET approach differs dramatically from confrontational treatment strategies in which the therapist takes primary responsibility for "breaking down the client's denial." Miller (1989, p. 75) provided these contrasts between approaches:

Confrontation-of-Denial Approach	Motivational-Interviewing Approach
Heavy emphasis on acceptance of self as "alcoholic"; acceptance of diagnosis seen as essential for change	Deemphasis on labels; acceptance of "alcoholism" label seen as unnecessary for change to occur
Emphasis on disease of alcoholism which reduces personal choice and control	Emphasis on personal choice regarding future use of alcohol and other drugs
Therapist presents perceived evidence of alcoholism in an attempt to convince the client of the diagnosis	Therapist conducts objective evaluation but focuses on eliciting the client's own concerns
Resistance seen as "denial," a trait characteristic of alcoholics requiring confrontation	Resistance seen as an interpersonal behavior pattern influenced by the therapist's behavior
Resistance is met with argumentation and correction	Resistance is met with reflection

A goal of the ME therapist is to evoke *from the client* statements of problem perception and a need for change (see "Eliciting Self-Motivational Statements"). This is the conceptual opposite of an approach in which the therapist takes responsibility for voicing these perspectives ("You're an alcoholic, and you have to quit drinking") and persuading the client of the truth. The ME therapist emphasizes the client's ability to change (self-efficacy) rather than the client's helplessness or powerlessness over alcohol. As discussed earlier, arguing with the client is carefully avoided, and strategies for handling resistance are more reflective than exhortational. The ME therapist, therefore, does *not*—

■ Argue with clients.

■ Impose a diagnostic label on clients.

■ Tell clients what they "must" do.

- Seek to "break down" denial by direct confrontation.

- Imply clients' "powerlessness."

The MET approach also differs substantially from cognitive-behavioral treatment strategies that prescribe and attempt to teach clients specific coping skills. No direct skill training is included in the MET approach. Clients are not taught "how to." Rather, the MET strategy relies on the client's own natural change processes and resources. Instead of telling clients how to change, the ME therapist builds motivation and elicits ideas as to how change might occur. Thus, the following contrasts apply:

Cognitive-Behavioral Approach	**Motivational Enhancement Approach**
Assumes that the client is motivated; no direct strategies for building motivation for change	Employs specific principles and strategies for building client motivation
Seeks to identify and modify maladaptive cognitions	Explores and reflects client perceptions without labeling or "correcting" them
Prescribes specific coping strategies	Elicits possible change strategies from the client and significant other
Teaches coping behaviors through instruction, modeling, directed practice, and feedback	Responsibility for change methods is left with the client; no training, modeling, or practice
Specific problem-solving strategies are taught	Natural problem-solving processes are elicited from the client and significant other

(Miller and Rollnick 1991)

MET, then, is an entirely different strategy from skill training. It assumes that the key element for lasting change is a motivational shift that instigates a decision and commitment to change. In the absence of such a shift, skill training is premature. Once such a shift has occurred, however, people's ordinary resources and their natural relationships may well suffice. Syme (1988), in fact, has argued that for many individuals a skill-training approach may be inefficacious precisely because it removes the focus from what is the key element of transformation: a clear and firm *decision* to change (cf. Miller and Brown 1991).

Finally, it is useful to differentiate MET from nondirective approaches with which it might be confused. In a strict Rogerian approach, the therapist does not direct treatment but follows the client's direction wherever it may lead. In contrast, MET employs systematic strategies toward specific goals. The therapist seeks actively to create discrepancy and to channel it toward behavior change (Miller 1983). Thus MET is a directive and persuasive approach, not a nondirective and passive approach.

Nondirective Approach	**Motivational Enhancement Approach**
Allows the client to determine the content and direction of counseling	Systematically directs the client toward motivation for change
Avoids injecting the counselor's own advice and feedback	Offers the counselor's own advice and feedback where appropriate
Empathic reflection is used noncontingently	Empathic reflection is used selectively to reinforce certain points
Explores the client's conflicts and emotions as they are currently	Seeks to create and amplify the client's discrepancy in order to enhance motivation for change

(Miller and Rollnick 1991

Practical Strategies

Phase 1: Building Motivation for Change

Motivational counseling can be divided into two major phases: building motivation for change and strengthening commitment to change (Miller and Rollnick 1991). The early phase of MET focuses on developing clients' motivation to make a change in their drinking. Clients will vary widely in their readiness to change. Some may come to treatment largely decided and determined to change, but the following processes should nevertheless be pursued in order to explore the depth of such apparent motivation and to begin consolidating commitment. Others will be reluctant or even hostile at the outset. At the extreme, some true precontemplators may be coerced into treatment by family, employer, or legal authorities. Most clients, however, are likely to enter the treatment process somewhere in the contemplation stage. They may already be dabbling with taking action but still need consolidation of motivation for change.

This phase may be thought of as tipping the motivational balance (Janis and Mann 1977; Miller 1989; Miller et al. 1988). One side of the seesaw favors status quo (i.e., continued drinking as before), whereas the other favors change. The former side of the decisional balance is weighed down by perceived positive benefits from drinking and feared consequences of change. Weights on the other side consist of perceived benefits of changing one's drinking and feared consequences of continuing unchanged. Your task is to shift the balance in favor of change. Eight strategies toward this end (Miller and Rollnick 1991) are outlined in this section.

Eliciting Self-Motivational Statements

There is truth to the saying that we can "talk ourselves into" a change. Motivational psychology has amply demonstrated that when people are subtly enticed to speak or act in a new way, their beliefs and values tend to shift in that direction. This phenomenon has sometimes been described as cognitive dissonance (Festinger 1957). Self-perception theory (Bem 1965, 1967, 1972), an alternative account of this phenomenon, might be summarized: "As I hear myself talk, I learn what I believe." That is, the words which come out of a person's mouth are quite persuasive to that person—more so, perhaps, than words spoken by another. "If I say it, and no one has forced me to say it, then I must believe it!"

If this is so, then the worst persuasion strategy is one that evokes defensive argumentation from the person. Head-on confrontation is rarely an effective sales technique ("Your children are educationally deprived, and you will be an irresponsible parent if you don't buy this encyclopedia"). This is a flawed approach not only because it evokes hostility, but also because it provokes the client to verbalize precisely the wrong set of statements. An aggressive argument that "You're an alcoholic and you have to stop drinking" will usually evoke a predictable set of responses: "No I'm not, and no I don't." Unfortunately, counselors are sometimes trained to understand such a response as client "denial" and to push all the harder. The likely result is a high level of client resistance.

The positive side of the coin is that the ME therapist seeks to elicit from the client certain kinds of statements that can be considered, within this view, to be self-motivating (Miller 1983). These include statements of—

■ Being open to input about drinking.

■ Acknowledging real or potential problems related to drinking

■ Expressing a need, desire, or willingness to change.

There are several ways to elicit such statements from clients. One is to ask for them directly, via open-ended questions. Some examples:

■ I assume, from the fact that you are here, that you have been having some concerns or difficulties related to your drinking. Tell me about those.

■ Tell me a little about your drinking. What do you like about drinking'? What's positive about drinking for you? And what's the other side? What are your worries about drinking?

■ Tell me what you've noticed about your drinking. How has it changed over time? What things have you noticed that concern you, that you think could be problems, or might become problems?

■ What have other people told you about your drinking? What are other people worried about? (If a spouse or significant other is present, this can be asked directly.)

■ What makes you think that perhaps you need to make a change in your drinking?

Once this process is rolling, simply keep it going by using reflective listening (see below), by asking for examples, by asking "What else?," and so forth. If it bogs down, you can inventory general areas such as—

- *Tolerance*—does the client seem to be able to drink more than other people without showing as much effect?

- *Memory*—has the client had periods of not remembering what happened while drinking or other memory problems?

- *Relationships*—has drinking affected relationships with spouse, family, or friends?

- *Health*—is the client aware of any health problems related to using alcohol?

- *Legal*—have there been any arrests or other brushes with the law because of behavior while drinking?

- *Financial*—has drinking contributed to money problems?

Information from the pretreatment assessment (to be used as feedback later) may also suggest some areas to explore.

If you encounter difficulties in eliciting client concerns, still another strategy is to employ gentle paradox to evoke self-motivational statements. In this table-turning approach, you subtly take on the voice of the client's "resistance," evoking from the client the opposite side. Some examples:

- You haven't convinced me yet that you are seriously concerned. You've come down here and gone through several hours of assessment. Is that all you're concerned about?

- I'll tell you one concern I have. This program is one that requires a fair amount of motivation from people, and frankly, I'm not sure from what you've told me so far that you're motivated enough to carry through with it. Do you think we should go ahead?

- I'm not sure how much you are interested in changing, or even in taking a careful look at your drinking. It sounds like you might be happier just going on as before.

Particularly in the presence of a significant other, such statements may elicit new self-motivational material. Similarly, a client may back down from a position if you state it more extremely, even in the form of a question. For example:

- So drinking is really *important* to you. Tell me about that.

- What is it about drinking that you really need to hang onto, that you can't let go of?

In general, however, the best opening strategy for eliciting self-motivational statements is to ask for them:

- Tell me what concerns you about your drinking.

- Tell me what it has cost you.

- Tell me why you think you might need to make a change.

Listening With Empathy

The eliciting strategies just discussed are likely to evoke some initial offerings, but it is also crucial how you *respond* to clients' statements. The therapeutic skill of accurate empathy (sometimes also called active listening, reflection, or understanding) is an optimal response within MET.

Empathy is commonly thought of as "feeling with" people, or having an immediate understanding of their situation by virtue of having experienced it (or something similar) oneself. Carl Rogers, however, introduced a new technical meaning for the term "empathy," using it to describe a particular skill and style of reflective listening (Rogers 1957, 1959). In this style, the therapist listens carefully to what the client is saying, then reflects it back to the client, often in a slightly modified or reframed form. Acknowledgment of the client's expressed or implicit feeling state may also be included. This way of responding offers a number of advantages: (1) it is unlikely to evoke client resistance, (2) it encourages the client to keep talking and exploring the topic, (3) it communicates respect and caring and builds a working therapeutic alliance, (4) it clarifies for the therapist exactly what the client means, and (5) it can be used to reinforce ideas expressed by the client.

This last characteristic is an important one. You can reflect quite selectively, choosing to reinforce certain components of what the client has said and ignoring others. In this way, clients not only hear themselves saying a self-motivational statement, but also hear you saying that they said it. Further, this style of responding is likely to encourage the client to elaborate the reflected statement. Here is an example of this process.

THERAPIST: What else concerns you about your drinking?

CLIENT: Well, I'm not sure I'm *concerned* about it, but I do wonder sometimes if I'm drinking too much.

T: Too much for . . .

C: For my own good, I guess. I mean it's not like it's really serious, but sometimes when I wake up in the morning I feel really awful, and I can't think straight most of the morning.

T: It messes up your thinking, your concentration.

C: Yes, and sometimes I have trouble remembering things.

T: And you wonder if that might be because you're drinking too much.

C: Well, I know it is sometimes.

T: You're pretty sure about that. But maybe there's more.

C: Yeah—even when I'm not drinking, sometimes I mix things up, and I wonder about that.

T: Wonder if . . .

C: If alcohol's pickling my brain, I guess.

T: You think that can happen to people, maybe to you.

C: Well, can't it? I've heard that alcohol kills brain cells.

T: Um-hmm. I can see why that would worry you.

C: But I don't think I'm an alcoholic or anything.

T: You don't think you're that bad off, but you do wonder if maybe you're overdoing it and damaging yourself in the process.

C: Yeah.

T: Kind of a scary thought. What else worries you?

This therapist is responding primarily with reflective listening. This is not, by any means, the *only* strategy used in MET, but it is an important one. Neither is this an easy skill. Easily parodied or done poorly, true reflective listening requires continuous alert tracking of the client's verbal and nonverbal responses and their possible meanings, formulation of reflections at the appropriate level of complexity, and ongoing adjustment of hypotheses. Optimal reflective listening suspends advice, agreement, disagreement, suggestions, teaching, warning, and questioning in favor of continued exploration of the client's own processes. (For more detail, see Egan 1982; Miller and Jackson 1985.)

It may be of further help to contrast reflective with alternative therapist responses to some client statements:

> CLIENT: I guess I do drink too much sometimes, but I don't think I have a *problem* with alcohol.

> - CONFRONTATION: Yes you do! How can you sit there and tell me you don't have a problem when...

> - QUESTION: Why do you think you don't have a problem?

> - REFLECTION: So on the one hand, you can see some reasons for concern, *and* you really don't want to be labeled as "having a problem."

> CLIENT: My wife is always telling me that I'm an alcoholic.

> - JUDGING: What's wrong with that? She probably has some good reasons for thinking so.

> - QUESTION: Why does she think that?

> - REFLECTION: And that really annoys you.

> CLIENT: If I quit drinking, what am I supposed to do for friends?

> - ADVICE: I guess you'll have to get some new ones.

> - SUGGESTION: Well, you could just tell your friends that you don't drink anymore, but you still want to see them.

> - REFLECTION: It's hard for you to imagine living without alcohol.

This style of reflective listening is to be used throughout MET. It is not to be used to the exclusion of other kinds of responses, but it should be your predominant style in responding to client statements. As the following sections indicate, however, the ME therapist also uses a variety of other strategies.

Finally, it should be noted that selective reflection can backfire. For a client who is ambivalent, reflection of one side of the dilemma ("So you can see that drinking is causing you some problems") may evoke the other side from the client ("Well, I don't think I have a *problem* really"). If this occurs, the therapist should reflect the ambivalence. This is often best done with a double-sided reflection that captures both sides of the client's discrepancy. These may be joined in the middle by the conjunction "but" or "and," though we favor the latter to highlight the ambivalence:

DOUBLE-SIDED REFLECTIONS

■ You don't think that alcohol is harming you seriously now, and at the same time you *are* concerned that it might get out of hand for you later.

■ You really enjoy drinking and would hate to give it up, and you can also see that it is causing serious problems for your family and your job.

Questioning

The MET style also includes questioning as an important therapist response. Rather than *telling* clients how they should feel or what to do, the therapist *asks* clients about their own feelings, ideas, concerns, and plans. Elicited information is then responded to with empathic reflection, affirmation, or reframing (see below).

Presenting Personal Feedback

The first MET session should always include feedback to the client from the pretreatment assessment. This is done in a structured way, providing clients with a written report of their results (Personal Feedback Report) and comparing these with normative ranges.

To initiate this phase, give the client (and significant other, if attending) the Personal Feedback Report (PFR), retaining a copy for your own reference. Go through the PFR step by step, explaining each item of information, pointing out the client's score and comparing it with normative data. The specific protocol used in Project MATCH is provided in appendix A along with suggestions for developing alternative batteries.

A very important part of this process is your own monitoring of and responding to the client during the feedback. Observe the client as you provide personal feedback. Allow time for the client (and significant other) to respond verbally. Use reflective listening to reinforce self-motivating statements that emerge during this period. Also respond reflectively to resistance statements, perhaps reframing them or embedding them in a double-sided reflection. Examples:

CLIENT: Wow! I'm drinking a lot more than I realized.

THERAPIST: It looks awfully high to you.

CLIENT: I can't believe it. I don't see how my drinking can be affecting me that much.

THERAPIST: This isn't what you expected to hear.

CLIENT: No, I don't really drink that much more than other people.

THERAPIST: So this is confusing to you. It seems like you drink about the same amount as your friends, yet here are the results. Maybe you think there's something wrong with the tests.

CLIENT: More bad news!

THERAPIST: This is pretty difficult for you to hear.

CLIENT: This gives me a lot to think about.

THERAPIST: A lot of reasons to think about making a change.

The same style of responding can be used with the client's significant other (SO). In this case, it is often helpful to reframe or emphasize the caring aspects behind what the SO is saying:

WIFE: I always thought he was drinking too much.

THERAPIST: You've been worried about him for quite a while.

HUSBAND: (weeping) I've *told* you to quit drinking!

THERAPIST: You really care about her a lot. It's hard to sit there and hear these results.

After reflecting an SO's statement, it is often wise to ask for the client's perceptions and to reflect self-motivational elements:

FRIEND: I never really thought he drank that much!

THERAPIST: This is taking you by surprise. (To client:) How about you? Does this surprise you, too?

WIFE: I've been trying to tell you all along that you were drinking too much. Now maybe you'll believe me.

THERAPIST: You've been worrying about this for a long time, and I guess you're hoping now he'll see why you've been so concerned. (To client:) What are you thinking about all this? You're getting a lot of input here.

Often a client will respond *nonverbally,* and it is possible also to reflect these reactions. A sigh, a frown, a slow sad shaking of the head, a whistle, a snort, or tears can communicate a reaction to feedback. You can respond to these with a reflection of the apparent feeling.

If the client is not volunteering reactions, it is wise to pause periodically during the feedback process to ask:

■ What do you make of this?

■ Does this make sense to you?

- Does this surprise you?

- What do you think about this?

- Do you understand? Am I being clear here?

Clients will have questions about their feedback and the tests on which their results are based. For this reason, you need to be quite familiar with the assessment battery and its interpretation. In Project MATCH, additional interpretive information is provided for the client to take home.

In the training videotape, "Motivational Interviewing," developed by and available from Dr. William Miller, this style of presenting assessment feedback to a resistant problem drinker is demonstrated.

Affirming the Client

You should also seek opportunities to affirm, compliment, and reinforce the client sincerely. Such affirmations can be beneficial in a number of ways, including (1) strengthening the working relationship, (2) enhancing the attitude of self-responsibility and empowerment, (3) reinforcing effort and self-motivational statements, and (4) supporting client self-esteem. Some examples:

- I appreciate your hanging in there through this feedback, which must be pretty rough for you.

- I think it's great that you're strong enough to recognize the risk here and that you want to do something before it gets more serious.

- You've been through a lot together, and I admire the kind of love and commitment you've had in staying together through all this.

- You really have some good ideas for how you might change.

- Thanks for listening so carefully today.

- You've taken a big step today, and I really respect you for it.

Handling Resistance

Client resistance is a legitimate concern. Failure to comply with a therapist's instructions and resistant behaviors within treatment sessions (e.g., arguing, interrupting, denying a problem) are responses that predict poor treatment outcome.

What is resistance? Here are some client behaviors that have been found to be predictive of poor treatment outcome:

- *Interrupting*—cutting off or talking over the therapist

- *Arguing*—challenging the therapist, discounting the therapist's views, disagreeing, open hostility

- *Sidetracking*—changing the subject, not responding, not paying attention

- *Defensiveness*—minimizing or denying the problem, excusing one's own behavior, blaming others, rejecting the therapist's opinion, showing unwillingness to change, alleged impunity, pessimism

What too few therapists realize, however, is the extent to which such client resistance during treatment is powerfully affected by the therapist's own style. Miller, Benefield, and Tonigan (in press) found that when problem drinkers were randomly assigned to two different therapist styles (given by the same therapists), one confrontational-directive and one motivational-reflective, those in the former group showed substantially higher levels of resistance and were much less likely to acknowledge their problems and need to change. These client resistance patterns were, in turn, predictive of less long-term change. Similarly, Patterson and Forgatch (1985) had family therapists switch back and forth between these two styles within the *same* therapy sessions and demonstrated that client resistance and noncompliance went up and down markedly with therapist behaviors. The picture that emerges is one in which the therapist dramatically influences client defensiveness, which, in turn, predicts the degree to which the client will change.

This is in contrast with the common view that alcoholics are resistant because of pernicious personality characteristics that are part of their condition. Denial is often regarded as a trait of alcoholics. In fact, extensive research has revealed few or no consistent personality characteristics among alcoholics, and studies of defense mechanisms have found that alcoholics show no different pattern from nonalcoholics (Miller 1985). In sum, people with alcohol problems do not, in general, walk through the therapist's door already possessing high levels of denial and resistance. These important client behaviors are more a function of the interpersonal interactions that occur during treatment.

An important goal in MET, then, is to avoid evoking client resistance (antimotivational statements). Said more bluntly, *client resistance is a therapist problem.* How you *respond* to resistant behaviors is one of the defining characteristics of MET.

A first rule of thumb is *never meet resistance head on.* Certain kinds of reactions are likely to exacerbate resistance, back the client further into a corner, and elicit antimotivational statements from the client (Gordon 1970; Miller and Jackson 1985). These therapist responses include—

- Arguing, disagreeing, challenging.

- Judging, criticizing, blaming.

- Warning of negative consequences.

- Seeking to persuade with logic or evidence.

- Interpreting or analyzing the "reasons" for resistance.

- Confronting with authority.

- Using sarcasm or incredulity.

Even direct questions as to why the client is "resisting" (e.g., Why do you think that you don't have a problem?) only serve to elicit from the client further defense of the antimotivational position and leave you in the logical position of counterargument. *If you find yourself in the position of arguing with the client to acknowledge a problem and the need for change, shift strategies.*

Remember that you want the *client* to make self-motivational statements (basically, "I have a problem" and "I need to do something about it"), and if you defend these positions it may evoke the opposite. Here are several strategies for deflecting resistance (Miller and Rollnick 1991):

- *Simple reflection.* One strategy is simply to reflect what the client is saying. This sometimes has the effect of eliciting the opposite and balancing the picture.

- *Reflection with amplification.* A modification is to reflect but exaggerate or amplify what the client is saying to the point where the client is likely to disavow it. There is a subtle balance here, because overdoing an exaggeration can elicit hostility.

  CLIENT: But I'm not an alcoholic, or anything like that.

  THERAPIST: You don't want to be labeled.

  C: No. I don't think I have a drinking problem.

  T: So as far as you can see, there really haven't been any problems or harm because of your drinking.

C: Well, I wouldn't say that.

T: Oh! So you do think sometimes your drinking has caused problems, but you just don't like the idea of being called an alcoholic.

■ *Double-sided reflection.* The last therapist statement in this example is a double-sided reflection, which is another way to deal with resistance. If a client offers a resistant statement, reflect it back with the other side (based on previous statements in the session).

C: But I can't quit drinking. I mean, all of my friends drink!

T: You can't imagine how you could not drink with your friends, and at the same time you're worried about how it's affecting you.

■ *Shifting focus.* Another strategy is to defuse resistance by shifting attention away from the problematic issue.

C: But I can't quit drinking. I mean, all of my friends drink!

T: You're getting way ahead of things. I'm not talking about your quitting drinking here, and I don't think you should get stuck on that concern right now. Let's just stay with what we're doing here—going through your feedback—and later on we can worry about what, if anything, you want to do about it.

■ *Rolling with.* Resistance can also be met by rolling with it instead of opposing it. There is a paradoxical element in this, which often will bring the client back to a balanced or opposite perspective. This strategy can be particularly useful with clients who present in a highly oppositional manner and who seem to reject every idea or suggestion.

C: But I can't quit drinking. I mean, all of my friends drink!

T: And it may very well be that when we're through, you'll decide that it's worth it to keep on drinking as you have been. It may be too difficult to make a change. That will be up to you.

Reframing

Reframing is a strategy whereby therapists invite clients to examine their perceptions in a new light or a reorganized form. New meaning is given to what has been said. When a client is receiving feedback that confirms drinking problems, a wife's reaction of "I knew it" can be recast from "I'm right and I told you so" to "You've been so worried about him, and you care about him very much."

The phenomenon of tolerance provides an excellent example for possible reframing (Miller and Rollnick 1991). Clients will often admit, even boast of, being able to "hold their liquor"—to drink more than other people without looking or feeling as intoxicated. This can be reframed (quite accurately) as a risk factor, the absence of a built-in warning system that tells people when they have had enough. Given high tolerance, people continue to drink to high levels of intoxication that can damage the body but fail to realize it because they do not look or feel intoxicated. Thus, what seemed good news ("I can hold it") becomes bad news ("I'm especially at risk").

Reframing can be used to help motivate the client and SO to deal with the drinking behavior. In placing current problems in a more positive or optimistic frame, the counselor hopes to communicate that the problem is solvable and changeable (Bergaman 1985; Fisch et al. 1982). In developing the reframe, it is important to use the client's *own* views, words, and perceptions about drinking. Some examples of reframes that can be utilized with problem drinkers are:

- *Drinking as reward.* "You may have a need to reward yourself on the weekends for successfully handling a stressful and difficult job during the week." The implication here is that there are alternative ways of rewarding oneself without going on a binge.

- *Drinking as a protective function.* "You don't want to impose additional stress on your family by openly sharing concerns or difficulties in your life [give examples]. As a result, you carry all this yourself and absorb tension and stress by drinking, as a way of trying not to burden your family." The implication here is that the problem drinker has inner strength or reserve, is concerned about the family, and could discover other ways to deal with these issues besides drinking.

- *Drinking as an adaptive function.* "Your drinking can be viewed as a means of avoiding conflict or tension in your marriage. Your drinking tends to keep the status quo, to keep things as they are. It seems like you have been drinking to keep your marriage intact. Yet both of you seem uncomfortable with this arrangement." The implication is that the client cares about the marriage and has been trying to keep it together but needs to find more effective ways to do this.

The general idea in reframing is to place the problem behavior in a more positive light, which in itself can have a paradoxical effect (prescribing the symptom), but to do so in a way that causes the person to take action to *change* the problem.

Summarizing

It is useful to summarize periodically during a session, particularly toward the end of a session. This amounts to a longer, summary reflection of what the client has said. It is especially useful to repeat and summarize the client's self-motivational statements. Elements of reluctance or resistance may be included in the summary, to prevent a negating reaction from the client. Such a summary serves the function of allowing clients to hear their own self-motivational statements yet a third time, after the initial statement and your reflection of it. Here is an example of how you might offer a summary to a client at the end of a first session:

> Let me try to pull together what we've said today, and you can tell me if I've missed anything important. I started out by asking you what you've noticed about your drinking, and you told me several things. You said that your drinking has increased over the years, and you also notice that you have a high tolerance for alcohol— when you drink a lot, you don't feel it as much. You've also had some memory blackouts, which I mentioned can be a worrisome sign. There have been some problems and fights in the family that you think are related to your drinking. On the feedback, you were surprised to learn that you are drinking more than 95 percent of the U.S. adult population and that your drinking must be getting you to fairly high blood alcohol levels even though you're not feeling it. There were some signs that alcohol is starting to damage you physically and that you are becoming dependent on alcohol. That fits with your concerns that it would be very hard for you to give up drinking And I remember that you were worried that you might be labeled as an alcoholic, and you didn't like that idea. I appreciate how open you have been to this feedback, though, and I can see you have some real concerns now about your drinking. Is that a pretty good summary? Did I miss anything?

Along the way during a session, shorter "progress" summaries can be given:

> So, thus far, you've told me that you are concerned you may be damaging your health by drinking too much and that sometimes you may not be as good a parent to your children as you'd like because of your drinking. What else concerns you?

Phase 2: Strengthening Commitment To Change

Recognizing Change Readiness

The strategies outlined above are designed to build motivation and to help tip the client's decisional balance in favor of change. A second major process in MET is to consolidate the client's commitment to change, once sufficient motivation is present (Miller and Rol'nick 1991).

Timing is a key issue—knowing *when* to begin moving toward a commitment to action. There is a useful analogy to sales here—knowing when the customer has been convinced and one should move toward "closing the deal." Within the Prochaska/DiClemente model, this is the determination stage, when the balance of contemplation has tipped in favor of change, and the client is ready for action (but not necessarily for maintenance). Such a shift is not irreversible. If the transition to action is delayed too long, determination can be lost. Once the balance has tipped, then, it is time to begin consolidating the client's decision.

There are no universal signs of crossing over into the determination stage. These are some changes you might observe (Miller and Rollnick 1991):

- The client stops resisting and raising objections.

- The client asks fewer questions.

- The client appears more settled, resolved, unburdened, or peaceful.

- The client makes self-motivational statements indicating a decision (or openness) to change ("I guess I need to do something about my drinking " "If I wanted to change my drinking, what could I do?").

- The client begins imagining how life might be after a change.

Here is a checklist of issues to assist you in determining a client's readiness to accept, continue in, and comply with a change program. These questions may also be useful in recognizing individuals at risk for prematurely withdrawing from treatment (Zweben et al. 1988).

- Has the client missed previous appointments or canceled prior sessions without rescheduling?

- If the client was coerced into treatment (e.g., for a drunk-driving offense), has the client discussed with you his or her reactions to this involuntariness—anger, relief, confusion, acceptance, and so forth?

- Does the client show a certain amount of indecisiveness or hesitancy about scheduling future sessions?

- Is the treatment being offered quite different from what the client has experienced or expected in the past? If so, have these differences and the client's reactions been discussed?

- Does the client seem to be very guarded during sessions or otherwise seem to be hesitant or resistant when a suggestion is offered?

- Does the client perceive involvement in treatment to be a degrading experience rather than a "new lease on life"?

If the answers to these questions suggest a lack of readiness for change, it might be valuable to explore further the client's uncertainties and ambivalence about drinking and change. It is also wise to delay any decisionmaking or attempts to obtain firm commitment to a plan of action.

For many clients, there may not be a clear point of decision or determination. Often, people begin considering and trying change strategies while they are in the later part of the contemplation stage. For some, their willingness to decide to change depends in part upon trying out various strategies until they find something that is satisfactory and effective. Then they commit to change. Thus, the shift from contemplation to action may be a gradual, tentative transition rather than a discrete decision.

It is also important to remember that even when a client appears to have made a decision and is taking steps to change, ambivalence is still likely to be present. Avoid assuming that once the client has decided to change, Phase 1 strategies are no longer needed. Likewise, you should proceed carefully with clients who make a commitment to change too quickly or too emphatically. Even when a person seems to enter treatment already committed to change, it is useful to pursue some of the above motivation-building and feedback strategies before moving into commitment consolidation.

In any event, a point comes when you should move toward strategies designed to consolidate commitment. The following strategies are useful once the initial phase has been passed and the client is moving toward change.

Discussing a Plan

The key shift for the therapist is from focusing on *reasons* for change (building motivation) to negotiating a *plan* for change. Clients may initiate this by stating a need or desire to change or by asking what they could do. Alternatively, the therapist may signal this shift (and test the water) by asking a transitional question such as:

- What do you make of all this? What are you thinking you'll do about it?

- Where does this leave you in terms of your drinking? What's your plan?

- I wonder what you're thinking about your drinking at this point.

- Now that you're this far, I wonder what you might do about these concerns.

Your goal during this phase is to elicit from the client (and SO) some ideas and ultimately a plan for what to do about the client's drinking It is not your task to prescribe a plan for *how* the client should change or to teach specific skills for doing so. The overall message is, "Only *you* can change your drinking, and it's up to you." Further questions may help: "How do you think you might do that? What do you think might help?" and to the SO, "How do you think you might help?" Reflecting and summarizing continue to be good therapeutic responses as more self-motivational statements and ideas are generated.

Communicating Free Choice

An important and consistent message throughout MET is the client's responsibility and freedom of choice. Reminders of this theme should be included during the commitment-strengthening process:

- It's up to you what you do about this.

- No one can decide this for you.

- No one can change your drinking for you. Only you can do it.

- You can decide to go on drinking just as you were or to change.

Consequences of Action and Inaction

A useful strategy is to ask the client (and SO) to anticipate the result if the client continues drinking as before. What would be likely consequences? It may be useful to make a written list of the possible negative consequences of not changing. Similarly, the anticipated benefits of change can be generated by the client (and SO).

For a more complete picture, you could also discuss what the client *fears* about changing. What might be the negative consequences of stopping drinking, for example? What are the advantages of continuing to drink as before? Reflection, summarizing, and reframing are appropriate therapist responses.

One possibility here is to construct a formal "decisional balance" sheet, by having the client generate (and write down) the pros and cons of change options. What are the positive and negative aspects of continuing with drinking as before? What are the possible benefits and costs of making a change in drinking?

Information and Advice

Often clients (and SOs) will ask for key information as important input for their decisional process. Such questions might include:

- Do alcohol problems run in families?

- Does the fact that I can hold my liquor mean I'm addicted?

- How does drinking damage the brain?

- What's a safe level of drinking?

- If I quit drinking, will these problems improve?

- Could my sleep problems be due to my drinking?

The number of possible questions is too large to plan specific answers here. In general, however, you should provide accurate, specific information that is requested by clients and SOs. It is often helpful afterward to ask for the client's response to this information: Does it make sense to you? Does that surprise you? What do *you* think about it?

Clients and SOs may also ask you for advice. "What do *you* think I should do?" It is quite appropriate to provide your own views in this circumstance, with a few caveats. It is often helpful to provide qualifiers and permission to disagree. For example:

- If you want my opinion, I can certainly give it to you, but you're the one who has to make up your mind in the end.

- I can tell you what I think I would want to do in your situation, and I'll be glad to do that, but remember that it's your choice. Do you want my opinion?

Being just a little resistive or "hard to get" in this situation can also be useful:

- I'm not sure I should tell you. Certainly I have an opinion, but you have to decide for yourself how you want to handle your life.

I guess I'm concerned that if I give you my advice, then it looks like I'm the one deciding instead of you. Are you sure you want to know?

Within this general set, feel free to give the client your best advice as to what change should be made, specifically with regard to—

■ What change should be made in the client's drinking (e.g., "I think you need to quit drinking altogether").

■ The need for the client and SO to work together.

■ General kinds of changes that the client might need to make in order to support sobriety (e.g., find new ways to spend time that don't involve drinking).

With regard to specific "how to's," however, you should *not* prescribe specific strategies or attempt to train specific skills. This challenge is turned back to the client (and SO):

■ How do you think you might be able to do that?

■ What might stand in your way?

■ You'd have to be pretty creative (strong, clever, resourceful) to find a way around that. I wonder how you could do it.

Again, you may be asked for specific information as part of this process (e.g., "I've heard about a drug that you can take once a day and it keeps you from drinking. How does it work?"). Accurate and specific information can be provided in such cases.

Emphasizing Abstinence

A client may well ask for information that you do not have. Do not feel obliged to know all the answers. It is fine to say that you do not know, but will find out. You can offer to research a question and get back to the client at the next session or by telephone.

Every client should be given, at some point during MET, a rationale for abstinence from alcohol. Avoid communications that seem to coerce or impose a goal, since this is inconsistent with the style of MET. Within this style, it is not up to you to "permit" or "let" or "allow" clients to make choices. The choice is theirs. You should, however, commend (not prescribe) abstinence and offer the following points in all cases:

■ Successful abstinence is a safe choice. If you don't drink, you can be sure that you won't have problems because of your drinking.

- There are good reasons to at least try a period of abstinence (e.g., to find out what it's like to live without alcohol and how you feel, to learn how you have become dependent on alcohol, to break your old habits, to experience a change and build some confidence, to please your spouse).

- No one can guarantee a safe level of drinking that will cause you no harm.

In certain cases, you have an additional responsibility to advise against a goal of moderation if the client appears to be deciding in that direction. Again, this must be done in a persuasive but not coercive manner, consistent with the overall tone of MET. ("It is your choice, of course. I want to tell you, however, that I'm worried about the choice you're considering, and if you're willing to listen, I'd like to tell you why I'm concerned. . ."). Among the reasons for advising against a goal of moderation are (Miller and Caddy 1977)—

- Medical conditions (e.g., liver disease) that contraindicate any drinking.

- Psychological problems likely to be exacerbated by any drinking.

- A diagnosis of idiosyncratic intoxication (DSM–III–R 291.40).

- Strong external demands on the client to abstain.

- Pregnancy.

- Use/abuse of medications that are hazardous in combination with alcohol.

- A history of severe alcohol problems and dependence.

The data in table 2 may be useful in determining cases in which moderation should be more strongly opposed. They are derived from long-term followups (3 to 8 years) of problem drinkers attempting to moderate their drinking (Miller et al. 1992). "Abstainers" are those who had been continuously abstinent for at least 12 months at followup; "asymptomatic drinkers" had been drinking moderately without problems for this same period. The "improved but impaired" group showed reduction in drinking and related problems but continued to show some symptoms of alcohol abuse or dependence. The AB:AS column shows the ratio, within each of four client ranges, of successful abstainers to successful asymptomatic drinkers.

In addition to the commendation of abstinence given in all cases, clients falling into ranges 3 or 4 should receive further counsel if they are entertaining a moderation goal. They can be advised that in a study

Table 2. Relationship of severity measures to types of treatment outcome

Severity		Treatment Outcome								Ratio AB:AS
Range	Scores	Total abstainers		Asymptomatic drinkers		Improved but impaired		Not improved		
		n	%	n	%	n	%	n	%	
Michigan Alcoholism Screening Test (MAST)										
1	0–10	3	14%	5	23%	8	36%	6	27%	3:5
2	11–18	7	21	7	21	6	18	14	41	1:1
3	19–28	10	40	2	8	4	16	9	36	5:1
4	29+	4	29	0	0	4	29	6	43	4:0
	Median	19.5		12.0		15.0		18.0		
	Mean	19.0		13.2		18.0		18.6		
	SD	7.6		6.2		12.5		9.1		
Alcohol Dependence Scale (ADS) Lifetime Accumulation of Symptoms										
1	0–14	2	8%	6	24%	9	36%	8	32%	1:3
2	15–20	4	14	4	14	4	14	16	57	1:1
3	21–27	11	35	6	19	5	16	9	29	11:6
4	28+	6	75	0	0	2	25	0	0	6:0
	Median	22.5		19.0		15.0		16.5		
	Mean	27.2		16.6		17.1		18.0		
	SD	14.5		7.8		7.7		5.4		

Source: Data from Miller et al. 1992.
NOTE: Asymptomatic = Drinking moderately with no evidence of problems
Improved = Drinking less, but still showing alcohol-related problems
AB/AS Ratio = Ratio of successful abstainers to asymptomatic drinkers

of problem drinkers attempting to moderate their drinking, people with severity scores resembling theirs were much more likely to succeed with abstinence. Those falling in range 4 can further be advised that in this same study, no one with scores like theirs managed to maintain problem-free drinking. Clients who are unwilling to discuss immediate and long-term abstinence as a goal might be more responsive to intermediate options, such as a short-term (e.g., 3-month) trial abstinence period, or tapering off of drinking toward an ultimate goal of abstention (Miller and Page 1991).

Dealing With Resistance

The same principles used for defusing resistance in the first phase of MET also apply here. Reluctance and ambivalence are not challenged directly but rather can be met with reflection or reframing. Gently paradoxical statements may also be useful during the commitment phase of MET. One form of such statements is permission to continue unchanged:

- Maybe you'll decide that it's worth it to you to keep on drinking the way you have been, even though it's costing you.

Another form is designed to pose a kind of crisis for the person by juxtaposing two important and inconsistent values:

- I wonder if it's really possible for you to keep drinking and still have your marriage, too.

The Change Plan Worksheet

The Change Plan Worksheet (CPW) is to be used during Phase 2 to help in specifying the client's action plan. You can use it as a format for taking notes as the client's plan emerges. Do not *start* Phase 2 by filling out the CPW. Rather, the information needed for the CPW should emerge through the motivational dialog described above. This information can then be used as a basis for your recapitulation (see below). Use the CPW as a guide to ensure that you have covered these aspects of the client's plan:

- *The changes I want to make are . . .* In what ways or areas does the client want to make a change? Be specific. It is also wise to include goals that are positive (wanting to begin, increase, improve, do more of something) and not only goals that could be accomplished through general anesthesia (to stop, avoid, or decrease behaviors).

- *The most important reasons why I want to make these changes are . . .* What are the likely consequences of action and inaction? Which motivations for change seem most impelling to the client?

- *The steps I plan to take in changing are . . .* How does the client plan to achieve the goals? How could the desired change be accomplished? Within the general plan and strategies described, what are some specific, concrete first steps that the client can take? When, where, and how will these steps be taken?

- *The ways other people can help me are . . .* In what ways could other people (including the significant other, if present) help the client in taking these steps toward change? How will the client arrange for such support?

■ *I will know that my plan is working if* . . . What does the client hope will happen as a result of this change plan? What benefits could be expected from this change?

■ *Some things that could interfere with my plan are* . . . Help the client to anticipate situations or changes that could undermine the plan. What could go wrong? How could the client stick with the plan despite these problems or setbacks?

Preprinted Change Plan Worksheet forms are convenient for MET therapists. Carbonless copy forms are recommended so you can write or print on the original and automatically have a copy to keep in the client's file. Give the original to the client and retain the copy for the file.

The Change Plan Worksheet

The changes I want to make are:

The most important reasons why I want to make these changes are:

The steps I plan to take in changing are:

The ways other people can help me are:
      Person   Possible ways to help

I will know that my plan is working if:

Some things that could interfere with my plan are:

Recapitulating

Toward the end of the commitment process, as you sense that the client is moving toward a firm decision for change, it is useful to offer a broad summary of what has transpired (Miller and Rollnick 1991). This may include a repetition of the reasons for concern uncovered in Phase 1 (see "Summarizing") as well as new information developed during Phase 2. Emphasis should be given to the client's self-motivational statements, the SO's role, the client's plans for change, and the perceived consequences of changing and not changing. Use your notes on the Change Plan Worksheet as a guide. Here is an example of how a recapitulation might be worded:

> Let me see if I understand where you are. Last time, we reviewed the reasons why you and your husband have been concerned about your drinking There were a number of these. You were both concerned that your drinking has contributed to problems in the family, both between you and with the children. You were worried, too, about the test results you received indicating that alcohol has been damaging your health. Your drinking seems to have been increasing slowly over the years, and with it, your dependence on alcohol. The accident that you had helped you realize that it was time to do something about your drinking, but I think you were still surprised when I gave you your feedback, just how much in danger you were.

> We've talked about what you might do about this, and you and your husband had different ideas at first. He thought you should go to AA, and you thought you'd just cut down on your drinking and try to avoid drinking when you are alone. We talked about what the results might be if you tried different approaches. Your husband was concerned that if you didn't make a sharp break with this drinking pattern you've had for so many years, you'd probably slip back into drinking too much and forget what we've discussed here. You agreed that that would be a risk and could imagine talking yourself into drinking alone or drinking to feel high. You didn't like the idea of AA, because you were concerned that people would see you there, even though, as we discussed, there is a strong principle of anonymity.

> Where you seem to be headed now is toward trying out a period of not drinking at all, for 3 months at least, to see how it goes and how you feel. Your husband likes this idea, too, and has agreed to spend more time with you so you can do things together in the evening or on weekends. You also thought you would get involved again in some of the community activities you used to enjoy during the day or maybe look for a job to keep you busy. Do I have it right? What have I missed?

If the client offers additions or changes, reflect these and integrate them into your recapitulation. Also note them on the Change Plan Worksheet.

Asking for Commitment

After you have recapitulated the client's situation and responded to additional points and concerns raised by the client (and SO), move toward getting a formal commitment to change. In essence, the client is to commit verbally to take concrete, planned steps to bring about the needed change. The key question (not necessarily in these words) is:

■ Are you ready to commit yourself to doing this?

As you discuss this commitment, also cover the following points:

■ Clarify what, exactly, the client plans to do. Give the client the completed Change Plan Worksheet and discuss it.

■ Reinforce what the client (and SO) perceive to be likely benefits of making a change, as well as the consequences of inaction.

■ Ask what concerns, fears, or doubts the client (and SO) may have that might interfere with carrying out the plan.

■ Ask what other obstacles might be encountered that could divert the client from the plan. Ask the client (and SO) to suggest how they could deal with these.

■ Clarify the SO's role in helping the client to make the desired change.

■ Remind the client (and SO) that you will be seeing the client for followthrough visits (scheduled at weeks 6 and 12) to see how he/she is doing.

If the client is willing to make a commitment, ask him/her to sign the Change Plan Worksheet and give the client the signed original, retaining a copy for your file.

Some clients are unwilling to commit themselves to a change goal or program. When clients remain ambivalent or hesitant about making a written or verbal commitment to deal with the alcohol problem, you may ask them to defer the decision until later. A specific time should be agreed upon to reevaluate and resolve the decision. The hope in allowing clients the opportunity to postpone such decisionmaking is that the motivational processes will act more favorably on them over time (Goldstein et al. 1966). Such flexibility provides clients with the opportunity to explore more fully the potential consequences of change and prepare themselves to deal with the consequences. Otherwise, clients may feel coerced into making a commitment before they are ready to take action.

In this case, clients may withdraw prematurely from treatment, rather than "lose face" over the failure to follow through on a commitment. It can be better, then, to say something like this:

> It sounds like you're really not quite ready to make this decision yet. That's perfectly understandable. This is a very tough choice for you. It might be better not to rush things here, not to try to make a decision right now. Why don't you think about it between now and our next visit, consider the benefits of making a change and of staying the same. We can explore this further next time, and sooner or later I'm sure it will become clear to you what you want to do. OK?

It can be helpful in this way to express explicit understanding and acceptance of clients' ambivalence as well as confidence in their ability to resolve the dilemma.

Involving a Significant Other

When skillfully handled by the therapist, the involvement of a significant other (spouse, family member, friend) can enhance motivational discrepancy and commitment to change. Whenever possible, clients in MET will be strongly urged to bring an SO to the first two MET sessions. At these meetings, the SO is actively engaged in the treatment process. Emphasis is placed on the need for the client and SO to work collaboratively on the drinking problem.

The MET approach recognizes the importance of the significant other in affecting the client's decision to change drinking behavior. This emphasis is based upon recent findings from a variety of alcohol treatment studies. For example, alcoholics seen in an outpatient setting were found more likely to remain in a spouse-involved treatment than in an individual approach (Zweben et al. 1983). Similarly, clients maintaining positive ties with family members fared better in a relationship enhancement therapy than in an intervention focused primarily on the psychological functioning of the client (Longabaugh et al. in press).

Involvement of an SO in the treatment process offers several advantages. It provides the SO an opportunity for firsthand understanding of the problem. It permits the SO to provide input and feedback in the development and implementation of treatment goals. The client and SO can also work collaboratively on issues and problems that might interfere with the attainment of treatment goals.

Goals for Significant Other Involvement

The following are general goals for the two SO-involved sessions:

- Establish rapport between the SO and the counselor.

- Raise the awareness of the SO about the extent and severity of the alcohol problem.

- Strengthen the SO's commitment to help the client overcome the drinking problem.

- Strengthen the SO's belief in the importance of his or her own contribution in changing the client's drinking patterns.

- Elicit feedback from the SO that might help motivate the problem drinker to change the drinking behavior. For example, a spouse might be asked to share concerns about the client's past, present, and future drinking. Having the spouse "deliver the message" can be valuable in negotiating suitable treatment goals.

- Promote higher levels of marital/family cohesiveness and satisfaction.

MET does not include intensive marital/family therapy. The main principle here is to elicit from client and SO those aspects of their relationship which are seen as most positive and to explore how they can work together in overcoming the drinking problem. Both client and SO can be asked to describe the other's strengths and positive attributes. Issues raised during SO-involved sessions can be moved toward the adoption of specific change goals. The counselor should *not* allow the client and SO to spend significant portions of a session complaining, denigrating, or criticizing. Such communications tend to be destructive and do not favor an atmosphere that motivates change.

Explaining the Significant Other's Role

Ideally, a client will be accompanied by an SO at the first session. The invitation to the SO should be made for the first session only, allowing you the flexibility to include or not include the SO in a second session. In the beginning of the session, the counselor should comment favorably on the SO's willingness to attend sessions with the problem drinker The rationale is then presented for having the SO attend:

- The SO cares about the client, and changes will have direct impact on both their lives.

- The SO's input will be valuable in setting treatment goals and developing strategies.

- The SO may be directly helpful by working with the client to resolve the drinking problem.

Emphasize that ultimate responsibility for change remains with the client but that the SO can be very helpful. It is useful here to explore tentatively, with both the SO and the client, how the SO might be supportive in resolving the drinking problem. You might ask the following:

— To SO: In what ways do you think you could be helpful to _____?

— To SO: What has been helpful to_____in the past?

— To client: How do you think_____ might be supportive to you now, as you're taking a look at your drinking?

Be careful not to "jump the gun" at this point. Asking such questions may elicit defensiveness and resistance if the client is not ready to consider change.

It is also important to remember that your role does *not* include prescribing specific tasks, offering spouse training, or conducting marital therapy. The MET approach provides the SO an opportunity to demonstrate support, verbally and behaviorally, and encourages the SO and client to generate their own solutions.

The Significant Other in Phase 1

In the first conjoint session, an important goal is to establish rapport—to create an environment in which the SO can feel comfortable about openly sharing concerns and disclosing information that may help promote change. The SO could also be expected to identify potential problems or issues that might arise which could interfere with attaining these objectives. To begin with, the counselor should attempt to "join" with the SO by asking about her or his own (past and present) experiences with the alcohol problem.

- What has it been like for you?

- What have you noticed about [client's] drinking?

- What has discouraged you from trying to help in the past?

- What do you see that is encouraging?

Emphasis should be placed on positive attempts to deal with the problem. At the same time, negative experiences—stress, family disorganization, job and employment difficulties—should be discussed and reframed as *normative*, that is, events that are common in families with an alcohol problem. Such a perspective should be communicated to the family member in the interview. The counselor might compare the SO's experiences to the personal stress experienced by families confronted with other chronic mental health or physical disorders such as heart disease, diabetes, and depression (without going into depth about such experiences).

Any concerns that the SO may have about the amount or type of treatment should be explored. Again, concerns expressed by family members or SOs should be responded to in an accepting, reflective, reassuring manner. SOs who express concern about the brevity of MET can be told about the findings of previous research (see table 1), namely, that people can and do overcome their drinking problems given even briefer treatment than this, and that making a firm commitment is the key.

The SO can often play an important role in helping the client resolve uncertainties or ambivalence about drinking and change during Phase 1. The SO can be asked to elaborate on the risks and costs of continued heavy drinking. For example, one spouse revealed during counseling that she was becoming increasingly alienated from her partner as a result of the negative impact that the drinking was having on their children. These questions, asked of the SO in the presence of the client, can be helpful in eliciting such concerns:

- How has the drinking affected you?

- What is different now that makes you more concerned about the drinking?

- What do you think will happen if the drinking continues as it has been?

Feedback provided by the SO can often be more meaningful to a client than information presented by the counselor. It can help the client mobilize commitment to change (Pearlman et al. 1989). In sharing information about the potential consequences of the drinking problem for family members, an SO may cause the client to experience emotional conflict (discrepancy) about drinking. Thus, the client may be confronted with a dilemma in which it is not possible both to continue drinking and to have a happy family. In this way, the decisional balance can be further tipped in favor of changing the drinking. One client became more conflicted about his drinking after his wife described the negative impact it was having on their children. He subsequently decided to give up drinking rather than to experience himself as a harmful parent.

At the same time, there is a danger of overwhelming the client if the feedback given by the SO is new, extremely negative, or presented in a hostile manner. Negative information presented by both the SO and the counselor may result in the client's feeling "ganged up on" in the session and could result in treatment dropout. The MET approach relies primarily upon instilling intrinsic motivation for change in the client rather than using external motivators such as pressure from SOs.

Therefore, when involving an SO in a session, it may be useful to go slowly in presenting material to the client. You may gauge the mood or state of clients by allowing them the opportunity to respond to specific items before soliciting further comments from the SO. You may ask whether the client is ready to examine the consequences (i.e., both personal and family concerns) that have followed from drinking. If feedback provided seems to be particularly aversive to the client, then it is important to intersperse affirmations of the client. The SO can be asked questions to elicit supportive and affirming comments:

- What are the things you like most about [client] when he/she is not drinking?

- What positive signs of change have you noticed that indicate [client] really wants to make a change?

- What are the things that give you hope that things can change for the better?

Supportive and affirming statements from the counselor and SO can further enhance commitment to change.

The client-centered nature of MET can be further emphasized by focusing on the client's responses to what the SO has offered. You might ask, for example:

- Of these things your husband has mentioned, which concern you most?

- How important do you think it is for you to deal with these concerns that your wife has raised?

Feedback provided from the assessment battery is also presented and discussed during SO-involved sessions. SOs can be asked for their own comments and reactions to the material being presented.

- What do you think about this? Is this consistent with what you have been thinking about [client's] drinking? Does any of this surprise you?

Such questions may help to confirm the SO's own perceptions about the severity of the alcohol problem as well as to clarify any misunderstandings about the problems being dealt with in treatment sessions.

The same strategies used to evoke client self-motivational statements can be applied with the SO as well. Once an agreement is reached about the seriousness of the problem, the counselor should explore how the SO might be helpful and supportive in dealing with the problem. Remember that MET is not a skill-training approach; the primary mechanism here is to elicit ideas from the SO and client about what could be done. In raising the awareness of the spouse about the client's drinking and related issues, the counselor mainly seeks to *motivate* the SO to play an active role in dealing with the problem.

The Significant Other in Phase 2

A spouse or other significant person who is attending sessions may be engaged in a helpful way in the commitment process of Phase 2. An SO can play a positive role in instigating and sustaining change, particularly in situations where interpersonal commitment is high. The SO can be involved in a number of ways.

Eliciting Feedback From the SO

The SO might provide further examples of the negative effects of drinking on the family, such as not showing up for meals, missing family celebrations such as birthday parties, embarrassing the family by being intoxicated, or alienating children and relatives. This is an extension of the SO's role in Phase 1.

Eliciting Support

The SO can comment favorably on the positive steps undertaken by the client to make a change in drinking, and you should encourage such expression of support. The SO may also agree to join with the client in change efforts (e.g., spending time in nondrinking settings).

Eliciting Self-Motivational Statements From the SO

This strategy should be employed in the second SO-involved session, after the client and SO have had a chance to reflect upon the information presented earlier. Clients may become less resistant after they have had more time to think about drinking and related issues (see "Asking for Commitment"). If, in the second interview, the client still appears to be hesitant or reluctant about dealing with the drinking and related matters, then an attempt should be made to acknowledge the feelings of frustration and helplessness experienced by the SO and to examine alternative ways to handle these frustrations:

> I know that you both want to do what's best for the family. However, there are times when there are differences in what the two of you

want. It can be frustrating when you can't seem to agree about what to do. (Turning to the spouse). In this case, you have a number of options. You can try to change your [husband's/wife's] attitude about drinking—I think you've tried that in the past without much success, right? Or you could do nothing and just wait. But that still leaves you feeling frustrated or helpless, maybe even hopeless, and that's no good. Or you can concentrate your energies on yourself and other members of your family and focus on developing a lifestyle for yourself that will take you away from drinking. What do you think about this third option? What things could you do to keep from being involved in drinking situations yourself and to develop a more rewarding life away from drinking?

In response to this question, one spouse determined that she would no longer accompany her spouse to the neighborhood tavern. Another went a step further and indicated that he would not be involved in any drinking-related activities with his wife. By eliciting such self-motivational statements and plans from SOs, it is possible to tip the client's balance further in favor of change (cf. Sisson and Azrin 1986).

Addressing the SO's Expectations

When goals and strategies for change are being discussed, SOs are invited to express their own views and to contribute to generating options. Any discrepancy between the client and SO with respect to future alcohol use should be addressed. Information from the pretreatment assessment may be used here to reach a consensus between client and SO (e.g., severity of alcohol problems, consumption pattern). If agreement cannot be reached, a decision may be delayed, allowing further opportunity to consider the issues (see "Asking for Commitment"). The objective is to establish goals that are mutually satisfactory. This can further reinforce commitment to the relationship as well as the resolution of alcohol problems.

Handling SO Disruptiveness

In some cases, SO involvement could become an obstacle in motivating the client to change and could even lead to a worsening of the drinking problem. It is important to identify these potentially problematic situations and to deal with them. The following scenarios are provided to illustrate circumstances where SO involvement might have a negative impact on MET:

■ Comments are made by the SO that appear to exacerbate an already strained relationship and to evoke further resistance from the client. Your efforts at eliciting verbal support from the SO are met with resistance. Your own efforts to elicit self-motivational statements from the client are hindered by SO remarks that foster client defensiveness.

- Comments made by the SO suggest an indifferent or hostile attitude toward the client. The SO demonstrates a lack of concern about whether the client makes a commitment or is attempting to resolve the drinking problem. The involvement of the SO appears to have little or no beneficial impact on eliciting self-motivational statements from the client. When the client does make self-motivational statements, the SO offers no support.

- The SO seems unwilling or unable to make changes requested by the client that might facilitate an improvement in the drinking pattern or their relationship. For example, despite strong requests from the client (and perhaps from you) to place a moratorium on negative communication patterns, the SO continues to harass the client about past drinking habits.

In these or other ways, involvement of the SO may prove more disruptive than helpful to treatment. The first approach in this case is to use MET procedures (reflection, reframing) to acknowledge and highlight the problematic interactions. If usual MET strategies do not result in a decrease in SO disruptiveness, intervene directly to stop the pattern. The following are potentially useful strategies for minimizing SO interference with the attainment of treatment goals and are consistent with the general MET approach. Note that these are departures from the usual procedures for MET spouse involvement and are implemented for "damage control."

- Limit the amount of involvement of the SO in sessions. You might explicitly limit SO involvement to (1) providing collateral information about the extent and pattern of drinking and (2) acquiring knowledge and understanding about the severity of the alcohol problem and the type of treatment being offered. Your interactions with the SO can be limited to clarifying factual information and ensuring that the SO has a good understanding of the client's alcohol problem and the plan for change. Typical structuring questions of this kind would be, "Do you understand what has been presented thus far?" "Do you have any questions about the material we have discussed so far?"

- Focus the session(s) on the client. You can announce that the focus of discussion should be on the client in terms of helping to resolve the concerns that brought him or her to treatment. Indicate that the drinking needs priority and that other concerns are best dealt with after the client has competed the MET program. Then direct the discussion to the client's concerns.

- Limit the SO's involvement in decisionmaking activities. If SO participation is problematic, allow the SO to be a witness to change, without requesting his or her direct involvement inside or outside of sessions. Avoid requesting input from the SO in formulating change goals and developing the plan of action. Do not request or expect SO affirmation of decisions made by the client with regard to drinking and change.

Remember that it is not necessary to invite the SO back for a second session. This is easiest if your initial invitation did not mention two sessions. Also, remember that the maximum number of sessions that may be attended by any SO is two (not including emergency sessions).

Phase 3: Followthrough Strategies

Once you have established a strong base of motivation for change (Phase 1) and have obtained the client's commitment to change (Phase 2), MET focuses on followthrough. This may occur as early as the second session, depending on the client's progress. Three processes are involved in followthrough: (1) reviewing progress, (2) renewing motivation, and (3) redoing commitment.

Reviewing Progress

Begin a followthrough session with a review of what has happened since your last session. Discuss with the client what commitment and plans were made, and explore what progress the client has made toward these. Respond with reflection, questioning, affirmation, and reframing, as before. Determine the extent to which previously established goals and plans have been implemented.

Renewing Motivation

The Phase 1 processes can be used again to renew motivation for change. The extent of this renewal depends on your judgment of the client's current commitment to change. This may be assessed by asking clients what they remember as the most important reasons for changing their drinking.

Redoing Committment

The Phase 2 processes can also be continued during followthrough. This may simply be a reaffirmation of the commitment made earlier. If the client has encountered significant problems or doubts about the initial plan, however, this is a time for reevaluation, moving toward a new plan and commitment. Seek to reinforce the client's sense of autonomy and self-efficacy—an ability to carry out self-chosen goals and plans.

The Structure of MET Sessions

The preceding sections outline the basic flow of MET from Phase 1 through Phase 3. This section addresses issues involved in planning and conducting the four specific sessions.

The Initial Session

Preparation for the First Session

Before treatment begins, clients are given an extensive battery of assessment instruments; the results are used as the basis for personal feedback in the first session. Appendix A discusses the instruments used in Project MATCH and various alternatives.

When you contact clients to make your first appointment, stress the importance of bringing along to this session their spouse or, if unmarried, someone else to whom they are close and who could be supportive. Typically, this would be a family member or a close friend. The critical criteria are that the SO is considered to be an "important person" to the client and that the SO ordinarily spends a significant amount of time with the client. Those designated as significant others are asked to participate in assessment and also to attend two (and only two) treatment sessions. If no such person is initially identified, explore further during the first session whether an SO can be designated. The intended support person is contacted either by the client or by the therapist (whichever is desired by the client) and invited to participate in the client's treatment. Again, the initial invitation should be for one visit only, to allow flexibility regarding a second session.

Also explain that the client must come to this session sober, that a breath test will be administered, and that any significant alcohol in the breath will require rescheduling. All MET sessions are preceded by a breath alcohol test to ensure sobriety. The client's blood alcohol concentration must be no higher than .05 (50 mg%) in order to proceed. Otherwise, the session must be rescheduled.

Presenting the Rationale and Limits of Treatment

The MET approach may be surprising for some clients, who come with an expectation of being led step by step through an intensive process of therapist-directed change (Edwards and Orford 1977). For this reason, you must be prepared to give a clear and persuasive explanation of the rationale for this approach. The timing of this rationale is a matter for your own judgment. It may not be necessary at the outset of MET. At least *some* structuring of what to expect, however, should be given to the client at the beginning of the first session. Here is an example of what you might say:

> Before we begin, let me just explain a little about how we will be working together. You have already spent time completing the tests that we need, and we appreciate the effort you put into that process. We'll make good use of the information from those tests today. This is the first of four sessions that we will be spending together, during which we'll take a close look together at your situation. I hope that you'll find these four sessions interesting and helpful.

> I should also explain right up front that I'm not going to be changing you. I hope that I can help you think about your present situation and consider what, if anything, you might want to do, but if there is any changing, you will be the one who does it. Nobody can tell you what to do; nobody can make you change. I'll be giving you a lot of information about yourself and maybe some advice, but what you do with all of that after our four sessions together is completely up to you. I couldn't change you if I wanted to. The only person who can decide whether and how you change is *you*. How does that sound to you?

Many clients will find this a very comfortable and compatible approach. Some, in fact, will express relief, having feared being castigated or coerced. Other clients or their significant others, however, may be uneasy with this approach and may need additional explanation and assurance. Here are several lines of followup discussion in such cases:

- Even with very extensive kinds of treatment, it is still the person who, in the end, decides what happens. *You* will determine what happens with your drinking.

- Longer and shorter treatment programs don't seem to produce different results. People in longer or more intensive programs don't do any better, overall, than those getting good consultation like this. Again, no one can "do it to you." In fact, many people change their drinking or quit smoking without any formal treatment at all.

- You are not alone. We will be keeping in touch with you to see how you are doing. If at followup visits, you still need more help, this can be arranged.

- You can call if you need to. I'm available here by telephone.

- I understand your worries, and it's perfectly understandable that you would be unsure at this point. Let's just get started, and we'll see where we are after we've had a chance to work together.

After this introduction, start with a brief structuring of the first session and, if applicable, the SO's role in this process (refer to the section on "Involving a Significant Other"). Tell the client (and SO) that you will be giving them feedback from the assessment instruments they completed, but first you want to understand better how they see the client's situation. Then proceed with strategies for "Eliciting Self-Motivational Statements." Use reflection ("Listening With Empathy") as your primary response during this early phase. Other strategies described under "Affirming the Client," "Handling Resistance," and "Reframing" are also quite appropriate here. (The "Motivational Interviewing" videotape by Dr. Miller demonstrates this early phase of MET.)

When you sense that you have elicited the major themes of concern from the client (and SO), offer a summary statement (see "Summarizing"). If this seems acceptable to the client (and SO), indicate that the next step is for you to provide feedback from the client's initial assessment. Give the client a copy of the Personal Feedback Report and review it step by step (see "Presenting Personal Feedback"). Again, you should use reflection, affirmation, reframing, and procedures for handling resistance, as described earlier. You might not complete this feedback process in the first session. If not, explain that you will continue the feedback in your next session, and *take back the client's copy of the PFR* for use in your second session, indicating that you will give it back to keep after you have completed reviewing the feedback next week.

If you do complete the feedback process, ask for the client's (and SO's) overall response. One possible query would be:

- I've given you quite a bit of information here, and at this point, I wonder what you make of all this and what you're thinking

Both the feedback and this query will often elicit self-motivational statements that can be reflected and used as a bridge to the next phase of MET.

After obtaining the client's (and SO's) responses to the feedback, offer one more summary, including both the concerns raised in the first "eliciting" process and the information provided during the feedback (see "Summarizing"). This is the transition point to the second phase of MET: consolidating commitment to change. (Again, you will not usually get this far in the first session, and this process is continued in subsequent sessions.)

Using cues from the client and SO (see "Recognizing Change Readiness"), begin eliciting thoughts, ideas, and plans for what might be done to address the problem (see "Discussing a Plan"). During this phase, also use procedures outlined under "Communicating Free Choice" and "Information and Advice." Specifically elicit from the client (and SO) what are perceived to be the possible benefits of action and the likely negative consequences of inaction (see "Consequences of Action"). These can be written down in the form of a balance sheet (reasons to continue as before versus reasons to change) and given to the client. The standard commendation of abstinence is to be included during this phase at an appropriate time. If a high-severity client (range 3 or 4 in table 2) appears to be headed toward a moderation goal, this is also the time to employ the abstinence advice procedure outlined in "Emphasizing Abstinence." The basic client-centered stance of reflection, questioning, affirming, reframing, and dealing with resistance indirectly is to be maintained throughout this and all MET sessions.

This phase proceeds toward the confirmation of a plan for change, and you should seek to obtain whatever commitment you can in this regard (see "Asking for Commitment"). It can be helpful to write down the client's goals and planned steps for change on the Change Plan Worksheet. If appropriate, this plan can be signed by the client (and SO). Be careful, however, not to press prematurely for a commitment. If a plan is signed before commitment is firm, a client may drop out of treatment rather than renege on the agreement.

Ending the First Session

Always end the first session by summarizing what has transpired. The content of this summary will depend upon how far you have proceeded. In some cases, progress will be slow, and you may spend most of the first session presenting feedback and dealing with concerns or resistance. In other cases, the client will be well along toward determination, and you may be into Phase 2 (strengthening commitment) strategies by the end of the first session. The speed with which this session proceeds will depend upon the client's current stage of change. Where possible, it is desirable to elicit some client self-motivational statements about change within the first session and to take some steps toward discussing a plan for change (even if tentative and incomplete). Also discuss what the client will do and what changes will be made (if any) between the first and second sessions. Do not hesitate to move toward commitment to change in the first session if this seems appropriate. On the other hand, do not feel pressed to do so. Premature commitment is ephemeral, and pressuring clients toward change before they are ready will evoke resistance and undermine the MET process.

At the end of the first session, always provide the client with a copy of *Alcohol and You* (Miller 1991) or other suitable reading material. If feedback has been completed, also give the client the Personal Feedback Report and a copy of "Understanding Your Personal Feedback Report."

The Followup Note

After the first session, prepare a handwritten note to be mailed to the client. This is *not* to be a form letter, but rather a personalized message in your own handwriting. (If your handwriting is illegible, make other arrangements, but the note should be handwritten, not typed.)

Several personalized elements can be included in this note:

- A "joining message" ("I was glad to see you" or "I felt happy for you and your wife after we spoke today")

- Affirmations of the client (and SO)

- A reflection of the seriousness of the problem

- A brief summary of highlights of the first session, especially self-motivational statements that emerged

- A statement of optimism and hope

- A reminder of the next session

Here is an example of what such a note might say:

Dear Mr. Robertson:

This is just a note to say that I'm glad you came in today. I agree with you that there are some serious concerns for you to deal with, and I appreciate how openly you are exploring them. You are already seeing some ways in which you might make a healthy change, and your wife seems very caring and willing to help. I think that together you will be able to find a way through these problems. I look forward to seeing you again on Tuesday the 24th at 2:00.

Keep a copy of the note for your records.

Followthrough Sessions

The Second Session

The second session is scheduled 1 to 2 weeks after session 1 and should begin with a brief summary of what transpired during the first session. Then proceed with the MET process, picking up where you left off. Continue with the client's personal feedback from assessment if this was not completed during the first session, and give the client the PFR and a copy of "Understanding Your Personal Feedback Report" (see appendix A) to take home. Proceed toward Phase 2 strategies and commitment to change if this was not completed in the first session. If a firm commitment was obtained in the first session, then proceed with followthrough procedures.

At the end of the second session, in all cases, offer a closing summary of the client's reasons for concern, the main themes of the feedback, and the plan that has been negotiated (see "Recapitulation"). This is the closing of the second session. If no commitment to change has been made, indicate that you will see how the client is doing at the followup in 4 weeks and will continue the discussion at that point. In any event, remind the client of the third session at week 6. When a spouse or SO has been involved in the first two sessions, thank the SO for participating in those sessions and explain that the next two sessions will be with the client alone. If the SO was not involved in both of the initial sessions, he or she may return for the third session. (The SO's involvement is not to exceed two sessions.)

Sessions 3 and 4

Sessions 3 and 4 are to be scheduled for weeks 6 and 12, respectively. They are important as "booster" sessions to reinforce the motivational processes begun in the initial sessions. As before, the therapist does not offer skill training or prescribe a specific course of action. Rather, the same motivational principles are applied throughout MET. Specific use is made in each session of the followthrough strategies outlined earlier: (1) reviewing progress, (2) renewing motivation, and (3) redoing commitment. Sessions 3 and 4 do not include the SO, unless the SO has not already attended two sessions.

Because several weeks normally lapse between sessions 2 and 3 and between sessions 3 and 4, you should send the client a handwritten note or telephone the client a few days before the scheduled appointment. This serves as a reminder and also expresses continued active interest in your client.

Begin each session with a discussion of what has transpired since the last session and a review of what has been accomplished in previous sessions. Complete each session with a summary of where the client is at present, eliciting the client's perceptions of what steps should betaken next. The prior plan for change can be reviewed, revised, and (if previously written down) rewritten.

During these sessions, be careful not to assume that ambivalence has been resolved and that commitment is firm. It is safer to assume that the client is still ambivalent and to continue using the motivation-building strategies of Phase 1 as well as the commitment-strengthening strategies of Phase 2.

There should be a clear sense of continuity of care. The four sessions of MET should be presented as progressive consultations and as continuous with the research protocol's schedule of followup sessions. The initial sessions build motivation and strengthen commitment, and subsequent sessions serve as periodic checkups of progress toward change.

It can be helpful during sessions 3 and 4 to discuss specific situations that have occurred since the last session. Two kinds of situations can be explored:

- Situations in which the client drank

- Situations in which the client did not drink

Drinking Situations

If the client drank since the last session, discuss how it occurred. Remember to remain empathic and to avoid a judgmental tone or stance. Consistent with the MET style, do not prescribe coping strategies for the client. Rather, use this discussion to renew motivation, eliciting from the client further self-motivational statements by asking for the clients thoughts, feelings, reactions, and realizations. Key questions can be used to renew commitment (e.g., "So what does this mean for the future?" "I wonder what you will need to do differently next time?")

Nondrinking Situations

Clients may also find it helpful and rewarding to review situations in which they might have drunk previously or in which they were tempted to drink but did not do so. Reinforce self-efficacy by asking clients to clarify what they did to cope successfully in these situations. Praise clients for small steps, little successes, even minor progress.

Termination

Formal termination should be acknowledged and discussed at the end of the fourth session. This is generally accomplished by a final reca-pitulation of the client's situation and progress through the MET sessions. Your final summary should include these elements:

- Review the most important factors motivating the client for change, and reconfirm these self-motivational themes.

- Summarize the commitments and changes that have been made thus far.

- Affirm and reinforce the client for commitments and changes that have been made.

- Explore additional areas for change that the client wants to accomplish in the future.

- Elicit self-motivational statements for the maintenance of change and for further changes.

- Support client self-efficacy, emphasizing the client's ability to change.

- Deal with any special problems that are evident (see below).

- Remind the client of continuing followup sessions, emphasizing that these are an important part of the overall program and can be helpful in maintaining change.

Review, in session 4, the major points that have come up in the prior three sessions. It may be useful to ask clients about the worst things that could happen if they went back to drinking as before. Help clients look to the immediate future, to anticipate upcoming events or potential obstacles to continued sobriety.

Dealing With Special Problems

Special problems can arise during any treatment. The following are general troubleshooting procedures for handling some of the situations that may arise in delivering therapy in general as well as within a research context.

Treatment Dissatisfaction

Clients may report thinking that the assigned treatment is not going to help or wanting a different treatment. Under these circumstances, you should first reinforce clients for being honest about their feelings (e.g., "I'm glad you expressed your concerns to me right away."). You should also confirm that clients have the right to quit treatment at any time, seek help elsewhere, or decide to work on the problem on their own. In any event, you should explore the client's feelings further (e.g., "Whatever you decide is up to you, but it might be helpful for us to talk about why you're concerned"). Concerns of this kind that arise during the first session are probably reservations about an approach they have not yet tried. Typically, in randomized studies of multiple treatments, it is appropriate to assure the client that all of the treatments in the study are expected to succeed equally and that you will be offering all the help you can. No one can guarantee that any particular treatment will work, but you can encourage the client to give it a good try for the planned period and see what happens. You can add that should the problem continue or worsen, you will discuss other possible approaches.

If a client expresses reservations after two or three sessions, consider whether there have been new developments. Have new problems arisen? Did the plan for change that was previously developed with the client fail to work, and if so, why? Was it properly implemented? Was it tried long enough? Is there input or pressure from someone else for a change in approaches or for discontinuation of treatment? Is the client discouraged?

If the client's drinking problem has shown improvement but new problems, not previously identified, have appeared, these new problems can be discussed, following (and not departing from) the treatment procedures outlined above. The discussion of new problems and concerns, or a review of how prior implementation failed, can set the stage for continuation in treatment. You can suggest that it may be too early to judge how well this approach will work and that the client should continue for the 12-week duration. After that, if the client still feels a need for additional treatment, he or she could certainly obtain it.

If other parties are concerned about this treatment and are pressuring the client, you can explore this problem by following the treatment guidelines outlined above. It is also permissible for you to telephone the concerned party (with written consent from the client) to discuss the concerns and provide assurances, along the same lines as those outlined above for similar client concerns.

In Project MATCH, a limit of no more than two additional "emergency" sessions may be provided at the therapist's discretion. These must remain consistent with the MET guidelines provided in this manual and can be viewed as an extension or intensification of MET. The SO may be included in these sessions if appropriate, but the SO may never be seen alone. All sessions, including any emergency sessions, must be completed within 12 weeks of the first session. After that date, therapists are no longer permitted to see the client for any session, even if MET has not been completed.

A plan to provide a specific referral and help the client make contact was devised in Project MATCH in case all attempts to keep the client in treatment fail. Additional treatment may not be provided by any project therapist. Referral is made to an outside agency or to a therapist within the same agency who has no involvement in Project MATCH. A good procedure for accomplishing the referral is to telephone the agency or professional while the client is still in your office and make a specific appointment. For Project MATCH, this is discussed with the project coordinator or project director, because it has implications for the client's continuation in the study. In any event, the client is urged to participate in follow-up interviews as originally planned.

Missed Appointments

When a client misses a scheduled appointment, respond immediately. First try to reach the client by telephone, and when you do, cover these basic points:

- Clarify the reasons for the missed appointment.

- Affirm the client—reinforce for having come.

- Express your eagerness to see the client again.

- Briefly mention serious concerns that emerged and your appreciation (as appropriate) that the client is exploring these.

- Express your optimism about the prospects for change.

- Reschedule the appointment.

If no reasonable explanation is offered for the missed appointment (e.g., illness, transportation breakdown), explore with the client whether the missed appointment might reflect any of the following:

- Uncertainty about whether or not treatment is needed (e.g., "I don't really have that much of a problem")

- Ambivalence about making a change

- Frustration or anger about having to participate in treatment (particularly with clients coerced by others into entering the program)

Handle such concerns in a manner consistent with MET (e.g., with reflective listening, reframing). Indicate that it is not surprising, in the beginning phase of consultation, for people to express their reluctance (frustration, anger, etc.) by not showing up for appointments, being late, and so on. Encouraging the client to voice these concerns directly may help to reduce their expression in future missed appointments. Use Phase 1 strategies to handle any resistance that is encountered. Affirm the client for being willing to discuss concerns. Then summarize what you have discussed, add your own optimism about the prospects for positive change, and obtain a recommitment to treatment. It may be useful to elicit some self-motivational statements from the client in this regard. Reschedule the appointment.

In all cases, unless you regard it as a duplication of the telephone contact that might offend the client, also send a personal, individualized handwritten note with these essential points. This should be done within 2 days of the missed appointment. Research indicates that a prompt note and telephone call of this kind significantly increase the likelihood that the client will return (Nirenberg et al. 1980; Panepinto and Higgins 1969). Place a copy of this note in the clinical file.

This procedure should be used when any of the four appointments is missed. Three attempts (new appointments) should be made to reschedule a missed session.

Telephone Consultation

Some clients and their SOs will contact you by telephone between sessions for additional consultation. This is acceptable, and all such contacts should be carefully documented in the client's file. An attempt should be made to keep such contacts brief, rather than providing additional sessions by telephone. All telephone contacts must also comply with the basic procedures of MET. Specific change strategies should not be prescribed. Rather, your approach emphasizes elicitation and reflection.

Early in a telephone contact, you should comment positively on the client's openness and willingness to contact you. Reflect and explore any expressions of uncertainty and ambivalence that are expressed with regard to goals or strategies discussed in a previous session. It can be helpful to "normalize" ambivalence and concerns; for example: "What you're feeling is not at all unusual. It's really quite common, especially in these early stages. Of *course* you're feeling confused. You're still quite attached to drinking, and you're thinking about changing a pattern that has developed over many years. Give yourself some time." Also, reinforce any self-motivational statements and indications of willingness to change. Reassurance can also be in order during these brief contacts, e.g., that people really do change their drinking, often with a few consultations.

Crisis Intervention

The Project MATCH protocol provides guidelines on actions to be taken if the therapist is contacted by the client or SO in a condition of crisis. Others using this manual can adopt these guidelines as needed for their own protocols. These guidelines permit offering up to two special emergency sessions with the client (and SO) within the 12-week treatment period.

If at any time, in the therapist's opinion, the immediate welfare and safety of the client or another person is in jeopardy (e.g., impending relapse, client is acutely suicidal or violent), the protocol instructs the therapist to intervene immediately and appropriately for the protection of those involved, with appropriate consultation from the therapy program supervisor. This may include your own immediate crisis intervention as well as appropriate referral. In Project MATCH, the therapist's involvement in crisis interventions cannot exceed two sessions above and beyond those prescribed by the treatment condition. If a client's urgent needs require more additional treatment than this, referral is arranged.

Cases where there appears to be a worsening of the drinking problems or evidence of other new and serious difficulties (e.g., suicidal thoughts, psychotic behavior, violence) are referred to the onsite Project MATCH study coordinator for further evaluation and consultation. Based on his/her own evaluation and the defined procedures of the study, the coordinator determines what action is warranted and whether the client should be continued in the study. If alternative treatments are warranted, the coordinator is involved in making this determination.

Recommended Reading and Additional Resources

Clinical Descriptions

Edwards, G., and Orford, J. A plain treatment for alcoholism. *Proceedings of the Royal Society of Medicine* 70:344–348, 1977.

Egan, G. *The Skilled Helper: A Model for Systematic Helping and Interpersonal Relating.* 2nd ed. Monterey, CA: Brooks/Cole, 1982.

Ivey, A. Intentional Interviewing and Counseling. Monterey, CA: Brooks/Cole, 1982.

Miller, W.R. Motivational interviewing with problem drinkers. *Behavioural Psychotherapy* 11:147–172, 1983.

Miller, W.R. Increasing motivation for change. In: Hester, R.K., and Miller, W.R., eds. *Handbook of Alcoholism Treatment Approaches: Effective Alternatives.* New York: Pergamon Press, 1989. pp. 67–80.

Miller, W.R., and Jackson, K.A. "Not listening" and "Listening." In: *Practical Psychology for Pastors.* Englewood Cliffs, NJ: Prentice-Hall, 1985. pp. 31–59.

Miller, W.R., and Rollnick, S. *Motivational Interviewing.* New York: Guilford Press, 1991.

Miller, W.R., and Sanchez, V.C. Motivating young adults for treatment and lifestyle change. In: Howard, G., ed. *Issues in Alcohol Use and Misuse by Young Adults.* Notre Dame, IN: University of Notre Dame Press, in press.

Miller, W.R., and Sovereign, R.G. The check-up: A model for early intervention in addictive behaviors. In: Løberg, T., Miller, W.R., Nathan, P.E., and Marlatt, G.A., eds. *Addictive Behaviors: Prevention and Early Intervention.* Amsterdam: Swets and Zeitlin-ger, 1989. pp. 219–231.

Miller, W.R.; Sovereign, R.G.; and Krege, B. Motivational interviewing with problem drinkers: II. The drinker's check-up as a preventive intervention. *Behavioural Psychotherapy* 16:251–268, 1988.

Sanchez-Craig, M. Brief didactic treatment for alcohol and drug-related problems: An approach based on client choice. *British Journal of Addiction* 85:169-177, 1990.

van Bilsen, H.P.J.G., and van Ernst, A.J. Heroin addiction: Motivational milieu therapy. *International Journal of the Addictions* 21:707–713, 1986.

Demonstration Videotapes

Miller, W.R. *Motivational Interviewing.* Albuquerque, NM: University of New Mexico, 1989. Available from William R. Miller, Ph.D., Department of Psychology, University of New Mexico, Albuquerque, NM, USA 87131-1161. European format videotape available from the National Drug and Alcohol Research Centre, P.O. Box 1, University of New South Wales, Kensington, NSW 2033, Australia.

Motivation and Change. Set of two training videotapes available from the Addiction Research Foundation, 33 Russell Street, Toronto M5S 2S1, Ontario, Canada.

Rollnick, S. *I Want It But I Don't Want It: An Introduction to Motivational Interviewing.* Mind's Eye Video, 1989. European format only. Available from the Department of Psychology, Whitchurch Hospital, Cardiff, Wales, United Kingdom, CF4 7XB.

van Bilsen, H.P.J.G., and Bennet, G. *Motivational Interviewing in the Addictive Behaviours.* East Dorset Health Authority and Matakena Video Productions, 1987. Contact Gerald A. Bennett, Ph.D., 20 Newstead Road, Bournemouth, Dorset, United King-dom BH6 3HJ.

van Ernst, A. J., van Bilsen, H. P. J. G., and Schippers, G. M. *Motivation: A Demonstration Videotape on Motivational Interviewing. Part I: Problem Drinking; Part 2: Heroin Addiction.* Audi-Visuele dienst A-faculteiten, Catholic University, Nijmegen, the Netherlands, 1986.

Zweben, A. *Motivating the Problem Drinker for Treatment.* Toronto: Addiction Research Foundation, 1986.

References

Alcoholics Anonymous. *Alcoholics Anonymous: The Story of How Many Thousands of Men and Women Have Recovered From Alcoholism.* 3rd ed. New York: AA World Services, 1976.

Anderson, P., and Scott, E. The effect of general practitioners' advice to heavy drinking men. *British Journal of Addiction* 87:891–900, 1992.

Annis, H.M. Is inpatient rehabilitation of the alcoholic cost effective? Con position. *Advances in Alcohol and Substance Abuse* 5:175190, 1985.

Appel, C-P., and Miller, W.R. "The Self-Evaluation of Drinking." Unpublished instrument, University of New Mexico, 1984.

Bandura, A. Self-efficacy mechanism in human agency. *American Psychologist* 37:122–147, 1982.

Bern, D.J. An experimental analysis of self-persuasion. *Journal of Experimental Social Psychology* 1:199–218, 1965.

Bern, D. J. Self-perception: An alternative interpretation of cognitive dissonance phenomena. *Psychological Review* 74:183–200, 1967.

Bern, D. J. Self-perception theory. In: Berkowitz, L., ed. *Advances in Experimental Social Psychology.* Vol. 6. New York: Academic Press, 1972. pp. 1–62.

Bergaman, J.R. *Fishing for Barracuda: Pragmatics for Brief Systemic Therapy.* New York: W.W. Norton, 1985.

Chafetz, M.E. A procedure for establishing therapeutic contact with the alcoholic. *Quarterly Journal of Studies on Alcohol* 22:325–328, 1961.

Chafetz, M.E.; Blane, H.T.; Abram, H.S.; Clark, E.; Golner, J.H.; Hastie, E.L.; and McCourt, W.F. Establishing treatment relations with alcoholics: A supplementary report. *Journal of Nervous and Mental Disease* 138:390–393, 1964.

Chapman, P.L.H., and Huygens, I. An evaluation of three treatment programmes for alcoholism: An experimental study with 6– and 18-month follow-ups. *British Journal of Addiction* 83:67–81, 1988.

Chick, J.; Lloyd, G.; and Crombie, E. Counseling problem drinkers in medical wards: A controlled study. *British Medical Journal* 290:965–967, 1985.

Chick, J.; Ritson, B.; Connaughton, J.; Stewart, A.; and Chick, J. Advice versus extended treatment for alcoholism: A controlled study. *British Journal of Addiction* 83:159–170, 1988.

Elvy, G.A.; Wells, J.E.; and Baird, K.A. Attempted referral as intervention for problem drinking in the general hospital. *British Journal of Addiction* 83:83–89, 1988.

Festinger, L. *A Theory of Cognitive Dissonance.* Evanston: Row, Peterson, 1957.

Fisch, R; Weakland, J.H.; and Segal, L. *Doing Therapy Briefly.* San Francisco: Jossey-Bass, 1982.

Goldstein, A.P.; Heller, K.; and Sechrest, L. *Psychotherapy and the Psychology of Behavior Change.* New York: Wiley, 1966.

Gordon, T. *Parent Effectiveness Training.* New York: Wyden, 1970.

Harris, K.B., and Miller, W.R. Behavioral self-control training for problem drinkers: Components of efficacy. *Psychology of Addictive Behaviors* 4:82–90, 1990.

Heather, N.; Campion, P.D.; Neville, R.G.; and Maccabe, D. Evaluation of a controlled drinking minimal intervention for problem drinkers in general practice (the DRAMS scheme). *Journal of the Royal College of General Practitioners* 37:358–363, 1987.

Heather, N.; Whitton, B.; and Robertson, I. Evaluation of a self-help manual for media-recruited problem drinkers: Six month follow-up results. *British Journal of Clinical Psychology* 25:19–34, 1986.

Holder, H.D.; Longabaugh, R.; Miller, W.R.; and Rubonis, A.V. The cost effectiveness of treatment for alcohol problems: A first approximation. *Journal of Studies on Alcohol* 52:517–540, 1991.

Janis, I.L., and Mann, L. *Decision Making.* New York: Free Press, 1977.

Kristenson, H.; Ohlin, H.; Hulten-Nosslin, M.B.; Trell, E.; and Hood, B. Identification and intervention of heavy drinking in middle-aged men: Results and follow-up of 24–60 months of long-term study with randomized controls. *Alcoholism: Clinical and Experimental Research* 7:203–209, 1983.

Longabaugh, R.; Beattie, M.; Noel, N.; Stout, R.; and Malloy, P. The effect of social investment on treatment outcome. *Journal of Studies on Alcohol,* in press.

Miller, W.R. Motivation for treatment: A review with special emphasis on alcoholism. *Psychological Bulletin* 98:84–107, 1985.

Miller, W.R. Motivation and treatment goals. *Drugs and Society* 1:133–151, 1987.

Miller, W.R.; Benefield, R.G.; and Tonigan, J.S. Enhancing motivation for change in problem drinking: A controlled comparison of two therapist styles. *Journal of Consulting and Clinical Psychology*, in press.

Miller, W.R., and Brown, J.M. Self-regulation as a conceptual basis for the prevention and treatment of addictive behaviors. In: Heather, N.; Miller, W.R.; and Greeley, J., eds. *Self-Control and the Addictive Behaviours.* Sydney: Pergamon Press Australia, 1991. pp. 3–79.

Miller, W.R., and Caddy, G.R. Abstinence and controlled drinking in the treatment of problem drinkers. *Journal of Studies on Alcohol* 38:986–1003, 1977.

Miller, W.R.; Gribskov, C.J.; and Mortell, R.L. Effectiveness of a self-control manual for problem drinkers with and without therapist contact. *International Journal of the Addictions* 16:1247–1254,1981.

Miller, W.R., and Hester, R.K. Inpatient alcoholism treatment: Who benefits? *American Psychologist* 41:794–805,1986.

Miller, W.R.; Leckman, A.L.; Delaney, H.D.; and Tinkcom, M. Long-term follow-up of behavioral self-control training. *Journal of Studies on Alcohol* 53:249–261, 1992.

Miller, W.R., and Page, A. Warm turkey: Alternative routes to abstinence. *Journal of Substance Abuse Treatment* 8:227–232, 1991.

Miller, W.R., and Sanchez, V.C. Motivating young adults for treatment and lifestyle change. In: Howard, G., ed. *Issues in Alcohol Use and Misuse by Young Adults.* Notre Dame, IN: University of Notre Dame Press, in press.

Miller, W.R., and Sovereign, R.G. The check-up: A model for early intervention in addictive behaviors. In: Løberg, T.; Miller, W.R.; Nathan, P.E.; and Marlatt, G.A., eds. *Addictive Behaviors: Prevention and Early Intervention.* Amsterdam: Swets and Zeitlinger, 1989. pp. 219–231.

Miller, W.R., and Taylor, C.A. Relative effectiveness of bibliotherapy, individual and group self-control training in the treatment of problem drinkers. *Addictive Behaviors* 5:13–24, 1980.

Miller, W.R.; Taylor, C.A.; and West, J.C. Focused versus broad spectrum behavior therapy for problem drinkers. *Journal of Consulting and Clinical Psychology* 48:590–601, 1980.

Nirenberg, T.D.; Sobell, L.C.; and Sobell, M.B. Effective and inexpensive procedures for decreasing client attrition in an outpatient alcohol treatment program. *American Journal of Drug and Alcohol Abuse* 7:73–82, 1980.

Orford, J. Critical conditions for change in the addictive behaviors. In: Miller, W.R., and Heather, N., eds. *Treating Addictive Behaviors: Processes of Change.* Elmsford, NY: Pergamon Press, 1986. pp. 91–108.

Orford, J., and Edwards, G. *Alcoholism: A Comparison of Treatment and Advice, With a Study of the Influence of Marriage.* Oxford: Oxford University Press, 1977.

Panepinto, W.C., and Higgins, M.J. Keeping alcoholics in treatment: Effective follow-through procedures. *Quarterly Journal of Studies on Alcohol* 30:414–419, 1969.

Patterson, G.A., and Forgatch, M.S. Therapist behavior as a determinant for client noncompliance: A paradox for the behavior modifier. *Journal of Consulting and Clinical Psychology* 53:846–851, 1985.

Pearlman, S.; Zweben, A.; and Li, S. The comparability of solicited versus clinic subjects in alcohol treatment research. *British Journal of Addiction,* 84,523–532,1989.

Persson, J., and Magnusson, P.—H. Early intervention in patients with excessive consumption of alcohol: A controlled study. *Alcohol* 6:403–408, 1989.

Prochaska, J.O., and DiClemente, C.C. Transtheoretical therapy toward a more integrative model of change. *Psychotherapy: Theory, Research and Practice* 19:276–288, 1982.

Prochaska, J.O., and DiClemente, C.C. *The Transtheoretical Approach: Crossing Traditional Boundaries of Therapy.* Homewood, IL: Dow Jones/Irwin, 1984.

Prochaska, J.O., and DiClemente, C.C. Processes and stages of change in smoking, weight control, and psychological distress. In: Schiffman, S., and Wills, T., eds. *Coping and Substance Abuse.* New York: Academic Press, 1985. pp. 319–345.

Prochaska, J.O., and DiClemente, C.C. Toward a comprehensive model of change. In: Miller, W.R., and Heather, N., eds. *Treating Addictive Behaviors: Processes of Change.* New York: Plenum Press, 1986. pp. 3–27.

Robertson, I.; Heather, N.; Dzialdowski, A.; Crawford, J.; and Winton, M. A comparison of minimal versus intensive controlled drinking treatment interventions for problem drinkers. *British Journal of Clinical Psychology* 22:185–194, 1986.

Rogers, C.R. The necessary and sufficient conditions for therapeutic personality change. *Journal of Consulting Psychology* 21:95–103, 1957.

Rogers, C.R. A theory of therapy, personality, and interpersonal relationships as developed in the client-centered framework. In: Koch, S., ed. *Psychology: The Study of a Science.* Vol. 3. *Formulations of the Person and the Social Context.* New York: McGraw-Hill, 1959. pp. 184–256.

Romelsjö, A.; Andersson, L.; Barrner, H.; Borg, S.; Granstrand, C.; Hultman, O.; Hassler, A.; Kallqvist, A.; Magnusson, P.; Morgell, R.; Nyman, K.; Olofsson, A.; Olsson, E.; Rhedin, A.; and Wikblad, 0. A randomized study of secondary prevention of early stage problem drinkers in primary health care. *British Journal of Addiction.* 84:1319–1327, 1989.

Sannibale, C. The differential effect of a set of brief interventions on the functioning of a group of "early-stage" problem drinkers. *Australian Drug and Alcohol Review* 7:147–155, 1988.

Scott, E., and Anderson, P. Randomized controlled trial of general practitioner intervention in women with excessive alcohol consumption. *Drug & Alcohol Review* 10:313–321, 1990.

Sisson, R.W., and Azrin, N.H. Family-member involvement to initiate and promote treatment of problem drinkers. *Journal of Behavior Therapy and Experimental Psychiatry* 17:15–21, 1986.

Skutle, A., and Berg, G. Training in controlled drinking for early-stage problem drinkers. *British Journal of Addiction* 82:493–501, 1987.

Syme, S.L. "Changing Difficult Behaviors: How to Succeed Without Really Trying." Paper presented at a Symposium on Advancing Health Education, Mills College, Oakland, CA, Sept. 1988.

Truax, C.B., and Carkhuff, R.R. *Toward Effective Counseling and Psychotherapy.* Chicago: Aldine, 1967.

U.S. Congress, Office of Technology Assessment. *The Effectiveness and Costs of Alcoholism Treatment.* Washington, DC: the Office, 1983.

Valle, S.K. Interpersonal functioning of alcoholism counselors and treatment outcome. *Journal of Studies on Alcohol* 42:783–790, 1981.

Wallace, P.; Cutler, S.; and Haines, A. Randomised controlled trial of general practitioner intervention in patients with excessive alcohol consumption. *British Medical Journal* 297:663–668, 1988.

Zweben, A.; Pearlman, S.; and Li, S. Reducing attrition from conjoint therapy with alcoholic couples. *Drug and Alcohol Dependence* 11:321–331, 1983.

Zweben, A.; Pearlman, S.; and Li, S. A comparison of brief advice and conjoint therapy in the treatment of alcohol abuse: The results of the marital systems study. *British Journal of Addiction* 83:899–916, 1988.

Appendix A:
Assessment Feedback Procedures
by William R. Miller, Ph.D.

Preface

The instructions contained in appendix A refer to the assessment feedback components of Motivational Enhancement Therapy, as practiced in Project MATCH. It is not necessary, however, to use exactly the same assessment instruments as were employed in Project MATCH. The basic idea is to assess a range of dimensions, with particular emphasis on those likely to reflect early problems or risk. If you wish to replicate the exact procedures used in MATCH, information is provided at the end of this appendix for obtaining the needed instruments. You may, however, construct your own assessment battery and design a corresponding Personal Feedback Report (PFR) based on normative data for the instruments you have chosen. The PFR used in Project MATCH is reproduced following page 89.

In general, your assessment battery should sample a variety of potential problem and risk domains. Here is a brief list of pertinent domains, with examples of appropriate assessment approaches for each.

Alcohol Consumption

The volume of alcohol consumption is a primary dimension for assessment, because all other risk and problem domains are related to the quantity and frequency of use. There are four basic approaches for quantifying alcohol consumption.

Quantity/ Frequency Questionnaire

The simplest approach is to ask a few structured questions regarding the frequency (e.g., how many days per month does the person drink) and quantity of consumption (e.g., on a drinking day, how many drinks does the person have on average). Such questions can be aided by describing a standard drink unit (see Miller et al. 1991 for alternatives) or asking separately about different kinds of beverages (beer, wine, spirits, etc.). An advantage of this approach is that, unlike the others, it can be administered by paper and pencil questionnaire. This method appears to underestimate actual consumption, however, and reliability and validity parameters have not been established.

Grid Averaging   A second approach is to reconstruct, by structured interview, a typical-drinking week and then account for episodes of drinking that deviate from this pattern. This approach was introduced by Miller and Marlatt (1984) and has been employed in a variety of studies.

Timeline Followback   A third and still more detailed approach is to reconstruct drinking by filling in an actual calendar for the past few weeks or months. Day by day drinking data are obtained, taking advantage of the memory-prompting value of a calendar (Sobell et al. 1980). The Form 90 approach used in Project MATCH (see below) represents a hybrid of the timeline and grid averaging methods.

Drinking Diary   Finally, individuals can be asked to keep a daily diary of alcohol consumption. These records can than be converted into quantitative data. A freeware computer program for this purpose has been developed by Markham, Miller, and Arciniega (see resource list at the end of this appendix).

Alcohol-Related Problems

As heavy drinking continues, life problems tend to accumulate. Some counting of such accumulation is a common measure of problem severity. Measures such as the Michigan Alcoholism Screening Test (MAST; Selzer 1971) combine life problems with other factors such as alcohol dependence symptoms and help seeking. Miller and Marlatt (1984) attempted to differentiate between common problematic consequences of heavy drinking and other life problems, which may or may not be alcohol related. The DRINC questionnaire (see below), developed for Project MATCH, is intended as a purer measure of negative consequences of drinking, apart from alcohol dependence signs.

Alcohol Dependence

The alcohol dependence syndrome is currently a central diagnostic concept. Severity of dependence represents a third dimension to be tapped in comprehensive assessment. A variety of alcohol dependence scales have been published. Skinner's Alcohol Dependence Scale (Skiller and Horn 1984) has been a popular instrument in North America, with strong pyschometric characteristics.

Physical Health

Heavy drinking also has predictable effects on physical health. The most common evaluation approach in this domain has been a serum chemistry profile, screening for elevations on variables commonly affected by excessive drinking. These include liver enzymes (SGOT, SGPT, GGT), mean corpuscular volume (MCV), and high-density lipoprotein (HDL). Blood pressure can also be screened, because heavy drinking contributes to hypertension.

Neuro-psychological Functioning

Knowledge of all of the above domains provides relatively little information about a person's cognitive functioning Problem drinkers have been found to be impaired on a variety of neuropsychological tests (Miller and Saucedo 1983). Both Project MATCH and other checkup and feedback interventions have included neuropsychological test results (see Miller and Sovereign 1989; Miller et al. 1988), although interventions can also be effective without the inclusion of neu-ropsychological testing (Bien and Miller submitted; Brown and Miller submitted). Tests that commonly show impairment include the Block Design and Digit/Symbol subtests of the Wechsler Adult Intelligence Scale, the Wisconsin Card Sorting Task, and Halstead-Reitan subtests including the Tactual Performance Test, the Trail-Making Test, and the Categories Test.

Risk Factors

Markers of high risk for alcohol problems can also be measured, apart from the individual's current level of use and its consequences Family history of alcohol/drug problems can be obtained by a variety of methods (e.g., Cacciola et al. 1987; Miller and Marlatt 1984). Of personality scales designed to detect correlates of risk for substance abuse, the MacAndrew scale has fared best in research, though others are available (Jacobson 1989; Miller 1976). Beliefs about alcohol, as assessed by Brown's Alcohol Expectancy Questionnaire, have also been found to be predictive of risk (Brown 1985).

Motivation for Change

Various approaches are available for measuring the extent of an individual's motivation for changing drinking. Some consist of simple Likert scales assessing commitment to abstinence or other change goals (e.g., Hall et al. 1990). Self-efficacy scales can be constructed to ask about confidence in one's ability to change. Respondents can be asked to rate the extent to which alcohol is helping or harming them on a range of life dimensions (Appel and Miller 1984). Stages of change derived from the Prochaska and DiClemente (1984) theoretical perspective were used as the basis for construction of the University of Rhode Island Change Assessment (Prochaska and DiClemente 1992; DiClemente and Hughes 1990) and the alcohol-specific Stages of Change Readiness and Treatment Eagerness Scale (SOCRATES; Miller).

Comprehensive Assessment Approaches

Several questionnaires and structured interview protocols provide a range of quantitative scores that can be compared with normative or diagnostic standards. None of these taps all of the above dimensions, but each provides a basis for judging status on several domains. The Alcohol Use Inventory (AUI; Horn et al. 1987) is a widely used and well-developed self-administered questionnaire that permits comparison of individual with normatived scores. The materials necessary to administer, score, and interpret the AUI are available from National Computer Systems, P.O. Box 1416, Minneapolis, MN 55440. The kit includes the AUI manual, forms, client test book, hand-scored answer key templates, and the AUI profile sheet, which summarizes the scores and can be given to the client. Structured interviews include the Addiction Severity Index (ASI; Cacciola et al. 1987), the Comprehensive Drinker Profile (CDP; Miller and Marlatt 1984, 1987), and the Form 90 interview developed for Project MATCH (see below).

The crucial point is that the battery of assessment procedures to be used as a basis for feedback can be tailored to the needs, time demands, and client characteristics of a program. What follows is but one example—from Project MATCH—of how assessment feedback can be done within the context of Motivational Enhancement Therapy.

The Project MATCH Assessment Feedback Protocol and Procedures for Completing The PFR

Prior to the first session with an MET client, the Personal Feedback Report is prepared by obtaining the pertinent data from the client's file. The following information from the Project MATCH assessment battery is used:

- AUDIT score from the Quickscreen

- Form 90–I (Initial Intake)

- ASI family history section

- MacAndrew scale score

- DRINC questionnaire

- Serum chemistry profile

- Neuropsychological test results

- Alcohol Use Inventory

BACCuS, an IBM–PC software program, is used for converting alcohol consumption data into standardized measures (Markham et al. submitted).

Alcohol Consumption

The first datum to be presented to the client is the number of standard drinks consumed during a week of drinking This calculation is available from Form 90–I, the Project MATCH interview protocol for quantifying alcohol consumption. Some degree of judgment is needed here, but remember that the goal is to provide clients with a fair picture of their alcohol consumption during a typical drinking week. If the Steady Pattern Chart has been completed (page 6), use line 38 as the number of standard drinks per week. If no Steady Pattern Chart has been completed, the client's drinking was too variable to provide a consistent weekly pattern. In this case, consult the Summary Statistics sheet. If the client abstained on fewer than 10 percent of days *during the 90-day window*, multiply the "Average SECs per drinking day" by 7 to obtain the number of standard drinks per week. Be sure you are examining the 90-day window and not the whole current period. If abstinent days exceed 10 percent, examine the calendar to determine whether these abstinent days mostly occurred within drinking weeks (e.g., no drinking on Monday through Wednesday) or whether they occurred in blocks in between periods of drinking (i.e., periodic drinker). In the former case, determine the typical number of drinking days in an average week and multiply this number of days by the Average SECs per drinking day (from the Summary Sheet) to obtain the number of standard drinks per week. In the latter case—a purely periodic drinker—determine from the calendar whether drinking episodes are normally at least 7 days in length. If so, use the same procedure as for the Steady Pattern Chart: multiply the Average SECs per drinking day by 7 to describe the number of standard drinks consumed during a typical week of drinking. If drinking episodes are typically shorter than 1 week (e.g., 3 days), multiply the average number of days in an episode by the Average SECs per drinking day (from the Summary Statistics). Again, remember that the guiding principle is to describe the number of standard drinks that the client consumed, on average, in a drinking week.

When you have obtained the client's average number of drinks per drinking week, use table 3 to obtain the client's percentile among American adults. Note the separate norms for men and women.

Estimated Blood Alcohol Concentration Peaks

The second set of data presented to Project MATCH clients consists of computer-projected blood alcohol concentration (BAC) peaks, based on alcohol consumption patterns reported on Form 90–I. These projections are computed by BACCuS and will normally have been completed by the research assistant who conducted the Form 90–I interview. Nevertheless, you should check these calculations using BACCuS. Any projected peak over 600 mg% should be reported as 600 mg%. The reasoning here is that projections above this level are likely to be overestimates, because actual BAC peaks above 600 mg%, though possible, are relatively rare.

The BAC peak for a typical drinking week is obtained from line 39 of Form 90–I. This is the highest intoxication peak from the typical drinking week grid. Note that it may be necessary to use the BACCuS program (Menu #3, BAC Peak for an Episode) to estimate BAC peaks for several different days in order to determine which yielded the highest BAC. It is not always obvious, from visual inspection, which period will produce the highest BAC peak. Where a day contains at least two periods of drinking separated by several hours (e.g., 6 drinks from noon until 2:00 pm and then 8 drinks from 7:00-11:00 pm), it is wise to try the BAC level for each period within the day, as well as for the whole day. (In the above example, you would run 6 drinks in 2 hours, 8 drinks in 4 hours, and 14 drinks in 11 hours. The resulting BAC projections for a 160-pound male would be 109, 124, and 152, respectively. In this case, the BAC of 152, from 14 drinks in 11 hours, would be used.) If the Steady Pattern Chart was not completed on 90–I, leave this line blank.

Table 3. Alcohol consumption norms for U.S. adults, in percents

Drinks per week	Total	Men	Women
0	35	29	41
1	58	46	68
2	66	54	77
3	68	57	78
4	71	61	82
5	77	67	86
6	78	68	87
7	80	70	89
8	81	71	89
9	82	73	90
10	83	75	91
11	84	75	91
12	85	77	92
13	86	77	93
14	87	79	94
15	87	80	94
16	88	81	94
17	89	82	95
18	90	84	96
19	91	85	96
20	91	86	96
21	92	88	96
22	92	88	97
23-24	93	88	97
25	93	89	98
26-27	94	89	98
28	94	90	98
29	95	91	98
30-33	95	92	98
34-35	95	93	98
36	96	93	98
37-39	96	94	98
40	96	94	99
41-46	97	95	99
47-48	97	96	99
49-50	98	97	99
51-62	98	97	99
63-64	99	97	>99.5
65-84	99	98	>99.6
85-101	99	99	>99.9
102-159	>99.5	99	>99.9
160+	>99.8	>99.5	>99.9

Source: 1990 National Alcohol Survey, Alcohol Research Group, Berkeley. Courtesy of Dr. Robin Room

The BAC peak for a heavier day of drinking is obtained from the Highest Peak BAC line of the Summary Statistics sheet. This represents the *highest* BAC peak reached during the 90-day period. This will never be lower than line 39 but may be the same as line 39. In this case, the number on both lines of section 2 would be the same.

Risk Factors

The third feedback panel on the PFR reflects five risk factors. Higher scores on these scales are associated with greater risk and severity of alcohol-related problems.

Tolerance Level

Tolerance level is inferred from the BAC peaks reached during the 90-day window. The rationale is that the higher the projected BAC peak, the higher the individual's tolerance. Use the higher of the two numbers in Section 2 to arrive at the classification:

0–60 mg%	Low tolerance
61–120 mg%	Medium tolerance
121–180 mg%	High tolerance
181 mg% +	Very high tolerance

Other Drug Risk

Other drug risk is judged from the lifetime use of other drugs, as reported on page 10 of Form 90–I. The rationale is that more frequent use of other drugs, or any use of drugs with higher dependence potential, is associated with greater risk for serious consequences and complications. Use the following classification system:

HIGH RISK	Any use of cocaine or crack
or	Any use of heroin, methadone, or other opiates
or	Frequent use (more than 3 months of at least once per week) of any other drug class except tobacco: Marijuana, Hash, THC Amphetamines, Stimulants, Diet Pills Tranquilizers Barbiturates
MEDIUM RISK	Any lifetime nonprescription use, but not frequent use (i.e., 3 months or less of weekly use) of any drug class except tobacco, opiates or cocaine: Marijuana, Hash, THC Amphetamines, Stimulants, Diet Pills Tranquilizers Barbiturates
LOW RISK	No use of other drugs (Code = 0 for all 10 drug classes except tobacco)

Family Risk

Family risk is judged from the family history of alcohol and other drug problems obtained in the ASI interview. The following weighting system is used to arrive at a total Family Risk score. Assign the designated number of points for *each* blood relative indicated to be positive for alcohol/drug problems:

If father positive	add 2 points
If mother positive	add 2 points
For each brother positive	add 2 points
For each sister positive	add 2 points
For each grandparent positive	add 1 point
For each uncle or aunt positive	add 1 point

Risk levels are judged according to the following classification system:

Family Risk Classifications

0–1	Low risk
2–3	Medium risk
4–6	High risk
7+	Very high risk

MacAndrew Scale

The MacAndrew Scale score can be obtained directly from this scale. The following classification system is used for risk:

MacAndrew Scale Risk Levels

0–23	Normal range; lower risk
24–29	Medium risk
30+	High risk

Age at Onset

Age at onset is the fifth risk factor in this panel. The rationale is that younger onset of problems is associated with a more severe course and symptomatology. Age at onset is calculated by the following procedure, using three items obtained from the DRINC (Drinker Inventory of Consequences) scale.

Calculating Age at Onset

1. Record these three numbers, if applicable, and sum them (from page 7 of Drinker Inventory of Consequences)

   Age of first regular intoxication (item 17): _____

   Age of first loss-of-control (item 18):   + _____

   Age of first alcohol problems (item 19):   + _____

   TOTAL   _____

2. Divide by the number of ages used in step 1:

   Age at onset   = _____

NOTE: If an age item was not recorded for the client (e.g., the client had never experienced loss of control), the average is based on the other two age items (divide by 2). If only one age item was completed, this constitutes the age at onset.

Risk level is judged according to this classification system:

Under 25.0   Higher risk

25.0–39.9   Medium risk

40.0 +   Lower risk

Problem Severity

The *AUDIT* score is recorded directly from this scale within the Quickscreen. The *DRINC* alcohol severity score is recorded directly from this questionnaire and is the sum of scores for the 55 *lifetime* consequences. Print the client's raw score for each of these two scales under the corresponding severity range (e.g., a 19 on the AUDIT would be printed under the HIGH descriptor, below the 16-25 range designation.)

The other information reviewed in the fourth panel is the profile of results from the AUI. Use the AUI Profile form, published by National Computer Systems, for this purpose. Circle the client's raw scores for all scales and connect the circles with straight lines. Do not cross the solid lines that divide categories.

Serum Chemistry

Obtain the client's serum chemistry scores on SGOT, GGTP, SGPT, uric acid, and bilirubin (total) from the lab report. Record these lab scores on the corresponding lines of the PFR. Interpretive ranges are shown on the PFR.

Neuro-psychological Test Results

A 5-point performance scale is used to interpret neuropsychological test results:

1   Well above average

2   Above average

3   Average

4   Below average

5   Well below average

The scoring systems below attempt to correct for effects of age and/or education level, based on available norms. The Shipley-Hartford Vocabulary test is used as a "hold" test that is less likely to be affected by alcohol, thus providing an estimate of the level of performance that would ordinarily be expected from an individual.

Shipley-Hartford Vocabulary Test (SV)

Use the *age-adjusted* score to obtain a normalized T-score, as specified in the revised Shipley-Hartford manual. Then use the following table to convert the T-score into our 1-5 scale:

≥63	1	Well above average
57–62	2	Above average
44–56	3	Average
38–43	4	Below average
≤37	5	Well below average

Shipley-Hartford Abstraction Test (SHVA)

Use the *age-adjusted* score to obtain a normalized T-score, as specified in the revised Shipley-Hartford manual. Then use the following table to convert the T-score into our 1–5 scale:

≥63	1	Well above average
57–62	2	Above average
44–56	3	Average
38–43	4	Below average
≤37	5	Well below average

Trail-Making Test, Form A (TMTA)

The score is the number of seconds to complete Form A.

	Age			
	20–39	40–49	50–59	60–69
1	≤ 21	≤ 22	≤ 25	≤ 29
2	22–26	23–28	26–29	30–35
3	27–41	29–44	30–48	36–66
4	42–49	45–58	49–66	67–103
5	≥ 50	≥59	≥ 67	≥ 104

Based on Lezak 1976, Table 17–6, page 558. Cutting points represent the 10th, 25th, 75th, and 90th percentiles.

Trail-Making Test, Form B (TMTB)

The score is the number of seconds to complete Form B.

	Age			
	20–39	40–49	50–59	60–69
1	≤ 45	≤ 49	≤ 55	≤ 64
2	46–55	50–57	56–75	65–89
3	56–93	58–99	76–134	90–171
4	94–128	100–150	135–176	172–281
5	≥ 129	≥ 151	≥ 177	≥ 282

Based on Lez, 1976, Table 17–6, page 558. Cutting points represent the 10th, 25th, 75th, and 90th percentiles.

Symbol Digit Modalities Test (SYDM)

The score for the Symbol Digit Modalities Test is the number of correct digits associated with their respective symbols within the 90-second written testing period.

Use this table if client has 12 years or less of education.

Age	1	2	3	4	5
18–24	≥ 67	63–66	47–62	42–46	≤ 41
25–34	≥ 65	61–64	46–60	41–45	≤ 40
35–44	≥ 64	60–63	44–59	39–43	≤ 38
45–54	≥ 62	57–61	39–56	33–38	≤ 32
55–64	≥ 55	51–54	36–53	31–35	≤ 30
65+	≥ 47	42–46	25–41	20–24	≤ 19

Use this table if client has 13 years or more of education.

Age	1	2	3	4	5
18–24	≥ 72	67–71	53–66	47–52	≤ 46
25–34	≥ 67	62–66	50–61	44–49	≤ 43
35–44	≥ 65	60–64	44–59	37–43	≤ 36
45–54	≥ 61	57–60	45–56	40–44	≤ 39
55–64	≥ 56	52–55	40–51	35–39	≤ 34
65+	≥ 55	49–54	33–48	27–32	≤ 26

Interpreting the PFR to Clients

Project MATCH therapists follow a systematic approach in discussing the Personal Feedback Report with clients. The general therapeutic style in giving MET feedback is illustrated in Dr. Miller's "Motivational Interviewing" videotape.

The original copy of the PFR is given to the client and a copy is retained for the therapist's file. The PFR consists of two pages of data from interviews and questionnaires plus the client's Alcohol Use Inventory Profile sheet. When the therapist has finished presenting the feedback, the client may take home the PFR plus a copy of "Understanding Your Personal Feedback Report." If a session ends partway through the feedback process, however, the therapist retains the original PFR, sending it home with the client only after the review of feedback is completed. Clients are given a copy of *Alcohol and You* at the end of the first session (a copy is included at the end of appendix A).

Therapists need to be thoroughly familiar with each of the scales included on the PFR. "Understanding Your Personal Feedback Report" provides basic information for the client. Here are some additional points helpful in reviewing the PFR with clients.

Alcohol Consumption

The idea of a standard drink is an important concept. Explain that all alcohol beverages—beer, wine, spirits—contain the same kind of alcohol, ethyl alcohol. They just contain different amounts of this drug. Use the "Standard Drink" graphic depicted in the client handout "Understanding Your Personal Feedback Report" to explain this. We are using, as a standard drink, any beverage that contains half an ounce of ethyl alcohol. Thus, the following beverages are each equal to one standard drink:

Beverage	Usual %	x	Ounces	=	Alcohol content
Beer	.05	x	10 oz	=	0.5 oz
Table wine	.12	x	4 oz	=	0.5 oz
Fortified wine	.20	x	2.5 oz	=	0.5 oz
Spirits					
80 proof	.40	x	1.25 oz	=	0.5 oz
100 proof	.50	x	1 oz	=	0.5 oz

Explain that the number of standard drinks per week is calculated from the client's own report of regular and periodic drinking patterns, converted into standard units as shown in the graphic.

The normative table provides an estimate of the client's standing among American adults of the same sex with regard to alcohol consumption. The conversion table provides percentile levels for various numbers of standard drinks per week, based on data from the 1990 National Alcohol Survey, provided by Dr. Robin Room of the Alcohol Research Group at Berkeley. A good explanation of this percentile figure is that, "This means you drink more than ____ percent of American [men/women] do, or that (100–X) percent of American (men/women) drink as much or more than you do."

Estimated BAC Peaks

The number of drinks consumed is only part of the picture. A certain number of drinks will have different effects on people, depending on factors like their weight and sex. The *pattern* of drinking also makes a difference: having 21 drinks within 4 hours on a Saturday is different from having 21 drinks over the course of a week (3 a day).

Another way to look at a person's drinking, then, is to estimate how intoxicated he or she becomes during periods of drinking Be clear here that we are discussing "intoxicated" in terms of the level of alcohol (a toxin) in the body and *not* the person's subjective sense of being drunk. It is common for alcoholics to be quite intoxicated (high BAC) but not to look or feel impaired.

The unit used here is milligrams of alcohol per 100 ml of blood, abbreviated "mg%." This is the unit commonly used by pharmacologists and has the additional convenience of being a whole number rather than a decimal (less confusing for some clients). If you or your client wish to compare this with the usual decimal expressions of BAC, simply move the decimal point three places to the left. Thus:

$80 \text{ mg}\% = .08$

$100 \text{ mg}\% = .10$

$256 \text{ mg}\% = .256$ and so on

Note that the "normal social drinking" range is defined as from 20–60 mg% in peak intoxication. In fact, the vast majority of American drinkers do not exceed 60 mg% when drinking.

Risk Factors

Introduce this section by explaining "risk." Elevated scores on risk factors are not predestination. A person with a family history of heart disease is not doomed to die of heart disease—*but* such a person needs to be extra careful about diet and exercise, for example, and to keep a careful eye for warning signs. The five scores in this section are markers of higher risk for serious problems with alcohol. They indicate a greater susceptibility to alcohol problems.

Tolerance

The behavioral effects as shown in "Understanding Your Personal Feedback Form" can be understood as the ordinary effects of various BAC levels. Because of tolerance, people may reach these BAC levels without feeling or showing the specific effects listed.

The presence of a high BAC level, especially if accompanied by a reported absence of apparent or subjective intoxication signs, is an indication of alcohol tolerance. This should be discussed with the client as a *risk factor*. That is, people with a high tolerance for alcohol have a *greater* risk of developing serious problems because of drinking! A few points to cover are—

- Tolerance is partly inherited, partly learned.

- For the most part, tolerance does not mean being able to get rid of alcohol at a faster rate (although this occurs to a small extent). Rather it means reaching high levels of alcohol in the body without feeling or showing the usual effects.

- Normal drinkers are sensitive to low doses of alcohol. They feel the effects of 1-2 drinks, and this tells them they have had enough. Other people seem to lack this warning system.

- A result of tolerance is that the person tends to take in large quantities of alcohol—enough to damage the brain and other organs of the body over time—without realizing it. Thus you damage yourself without feeling it. An analogy would be a person who loses all sensations of pain. While at first this might seem a blessing, in fact, it is a curse, because such a person can be severely injured without feeling it. The first sign that your hand is on a hot stove is the smell of the smoke. Similarly, for tolerant drinkers, the first signs of intoxication are felt at rather high BAC levels.

Other Drug Risk

A second risk factor to consider is other drug use. In essence, the more drugs the client is using, the greater the risk for problems, cross-tolerance, dependence, drug substitution (decreasing one but increasing another), and so forth. Discuss these risks with your client.

Family Risk

Evidence is now strong that alcohol problems run in families and are genetically influenced. Of course, many people develop alcohol problems without having a family history, but your risk is higher if you have blood relatives with alcohol problems. Any family history should be discussed with the client.

MacAndrew Score

Higher scores on the MacAndrew scale, a subscale of the MMPI, have been found for alcoholics than for normals or people with other psychological problems. Elevations on this scale have also been found to be predictive, in young people, of *later* development of alcohol problems.

This personality scale taps a variety of personal characteristics that are associated with higher risk of serious alcohol problems.

Age at Onset   Alcohol problems tend to be more severe when they begin at a younger age. Three items from the Drinker Inventory of Consequences are averaged to obtain an "age of onset" for alcohol difficulties. The younger this age, the greater the risk for developing severe problems if drinking continues. Young emergence of "loss of control" (difficulty stopping once started or in keeping one's drinking within planned limits), for example, may be an indicator of high risk for severe alcohol problems.

Problem Severity

Two measures from Project MATCH screening are used here to reflect overall alcohol problem severity. One is the AUDIT scale, developed by the World Health Organization and used in the Quickscreen. The other is the Drinker Inventory of Consequences. Explain that these scores are very broad, general measures of negative effects of drinking in an individual's life. Notice that the AUDIT focuses on recent patterns, whereas the DRINC measures lifetime effects.

Your larger task here is to review with the client his or her scores from the Alcohol Use Inventory. To do this, you should be thoroughly familiar with the manual (Horn et al. 1987), particularly chapter 6. It is helpful, in understanding and interpreting scales, to be familiar with the items that constitute each scale (see page 71 of the manual). Refer to (and provide the client with a copy of) the AUI Profile Sheet, available from National Computer Systems, Minneapolis, MN. Remember when interpreting elevations on the AUI that the reference population is *people already seeking treatment for alcohol problems*. Thus, a "low" score in the white (decile 1–3) range is low relative to people entering treatment for alcohol problems. Scores in the middle deciles (4–7; light grey) are by no means average for the general population. General population norms on most scales would be expected to fall in deciles 1–2. A possible exception is GREGARIOUS, where high scores reflect drinking in social settings—a common style for young American men.

Serum Chemistry

These five serum assays can be elevated by excessive drinking and thereby reflect the physical impact of alcohol on the body. It is noteworthy that many heavy and problematic drinkers have normal scores on serum assays. The physical damage reflected by elevations on these scales may emerge much later than other types of problems. Also, normal scores on these tests *cannot* be interpreted as the absence of physical damage from drinking. The destruction of liver cells near the portal vein where blood enters, for example, can occur before liver enzymes reflect a warning. When these scales are elevated, then, it is information to be taken seriously.

Therapists should clarify that, as a nonmedical professional, you are not qualified to interpret these findings in detail. Clients who are concerned and want more information should be advised to discuss their results with a physician. If possible, referral should be made to a physician who is knowledgeable about alcohol abuse. A physician in general practice who is not familiar with alcohol abuse may advise a patient that their elevations are "nothing to worry about," undermining the feedback process.

The following information will help explain to clients the basic processes underlying these assays and what they may mean.

SGOT/SGPT

Serum glutamic oxalcetic transaminase (SGOT; newer name: AST-aspartate animotransferase) and serum glutamic pyruvate transaminase (SGPT; newer name: ALT—alanine transferase) are enzymes that reflect the health of the liver. The liver is important in metabolism of food and energy and also filters and neutralizes poisons and impurities in the blood. When the liver is damaged, as happens from heavy drinking, it becomes less efficient in these tasks and begins to leak enzymes into the bloodstream. These two are general indicators, reflecting overall health of the liver.

GGTP

Serum gamma glutamyl transpeptidase is an enzyme found in liver, blood, and brain, which is more specifically sensitive to alcohol's effects. Elevations of this enzyme have been shown to be predictive of later serious medical problems related to drinking, including injuries, illnesses, hospitalizations, and deaths. This enzyme is often elevated first, with SGOT and SGPT rising into the abnormal range as heavy drinking continues.

Bilirubin (Total)

The liver is also importantly involved in the recycling of hemoglobin, the molecule which makes the blood red. Bilirubin is one breakdown product of hemoglobin. When the liver is not working properly, it cannot recycle hemoglobin efficiently, and the byproducts back up into the bloodstream and eventually into the brain. High bilirubin levels over time result in jaundice—yellowing of the skin. Elevations of bilirubin are not common, even among heavy drinkers, and are indicative of severe physical impact from alcohol.

Uric Acid

Uric acid is a waste product that results from the breakdown of RNA. Alcohol's damage to the liver reduces the kidney's ability to excrete uric acid, which then builds up in the bloodstream. High levels of uric acid result in gout, the painful inflammation of joints, particularly fingers and toes. Uric acid is also an important component of a certain type of kidney stones.

If your site is including other relevant assays in your serum chemistry package (e.g., HDL, MCV), these could be included on your feedback form.

Enzyme elevations can occur for reasons other than heavy drinking. GGTP, for example, can be elevated by cancer or hormonal changes. In this population, however, the most likely cause of an elevation is heavy drinking. In this case, these assays tend to return toward normal if the person ceases heavy drinking. Reductions in GGTP (by changed drinking) have been shown to be associated with dramatically reduced risk of serious medical problems.

Neuro-psychological Test Results

The last panel of assessment results in the Project MATCH MET feedback is from the brief neuropsychological testing. Scores on these tests range from 1 (well above average) to 5 (well below average). Scores of 4 are often interpreted as "suggestive" of cognitive impairment, and scores of 5 as "indicative" of cognitive impairment.

The first (SV) result is from the Shipley-Hartford Vocabulary test. It is included as a "hold" test to indicate the approximate level of cognitive functioning that would be *expected* for a particular individual. Performance on this test is not commonly affected by alcohol use. This score, then, gives you an approximate reference point with which to compare other performances.

The other four tests appear to be sensitive to the effects of alcohol on the brain. They tend to be impaired in heavy drinkers and often show substantial improvement over the first weeks and months of sobriety. No judgment can be made about a client's general neuropsychological functioning or "brain damage" from this brief set of tests. Rather, they are *indicators* of the types of cognitive impairment commonly related to heavy drinking.

The Trail-Making Test has two forms. Trails A is a follow-the-dot format that mainly tests psychomotor speed. Alcoholics tend to be impaired (slow) on this test, though normal scores are more common than on Trails B. Trails B requires not only test psychomotor speed but also a mental switching back and forth between two cognitive sets—numbers and letters. As a group, alcoholics are rather consistently impaired (slow) on this test.

The Symbol Digit Modalities test is a reversal of the more familiar Digit/Symbol subtest of the WAIS. It is a timed test requiring the copying of numbers that correspond to symbols. It is influenced not only by psychomotor speed but also by memory. Alcoholics tend to perform more poorly (complete fewer correct digits) than others on this scale.

Finally, the Abstraction scale of the Shipley-Hartford taps a cognitive capacity—verbal abstraction ability—that is commonly impaired in heavy drinkers. Lower scores are associated with more concrete thinking styles. The common observation in alcoholics is a poorer performance on Abstraction than on the Vocabulary scale of the Shipley.

Be aware of other factors that may have influenced performance. Speed on Trails and Symbol/Digit, for example, will be slowed by an injury to the writing hand or arm. Visual impairments will also slow performance on these tests.

The PFR form and the handout explaining the data on the PFR form as used in Project MATCH are provided as examples. These can be modified to suit the needs of other research studies.

Assessment Instruments Used in Project MATCH Feedback

Both published and newly developed assessment instruments were employed in Project MATCH as a basis for providing client feedback in Motivational Enhancement Therapy. The sources from which these instruments can be obtained are provided below.

Form 90

Form 90 is a family of assessment interview instruments designed to provide primary dependent measures of alcohol consumption and related variables. It is a structured interview procedure that yields quantitative indices of alcohol consumption, other drug use, and related variables during a specified period of time. These instruments were developed for use in Project MATCH, with the collaboration of all principal investigators in that project. A Form-90 manual and forms will be published when final protocols and initial psychometric data are available. While the instrument remains under development, a research citation should be in this form:

> Miller, W.R. "Form 90: Structured Assessment Interview for Drinking and Related Behavior." Unpublished manual for Project MATCH, National Institute on Alcohol Abuse and Alcoholism.

Until publication, requests for use should be addressed to William R. Miller, Ph.D., Department of Psychology, University of New Mexico, Albuquerque, NM 87131.

DRINC

The alcohol research field has lacked a consensus instrument for assessing negative consequences of drinking. The DRINC was designed as a survey schedule for evaluating the occurrence of negative consequences related to drinking during a particular period of time. Items that are typically recognized as components of alcohol dependence syndrome (e.g., craving, blackouts) are intentionally omitted from this scale in an attempt to disaggregate dependence symptoms and negative life consequences. The DRINC also avoids the confounding, apparent in prior questionnaires (e.g., MAST), of recent consequences with lifetime ("ever") consequences or treatment experiences. The DRINC is therefore meant to be useful for parallel assessment of pretreatment and posttreatment consequences of drinking. It yields problem scores for "ever" (lifetime) and for a specific timeframe (past 3 months), which can be adjusted.

The DRINC should be regarded as an experimental instrument, currently in development. An initial psychometric study with 299 drinkers found good internal consistency (Cronbach alpha = .92 for "ever" and .90 for past 3 months). Initial analyses further indicate the negative consequences as a construct is related to but not identical with alcohol dependence and alcohol consumption. Correlations with Skinner's Alcohol Dependence Scale were .58 for Ever and .56 for Past 3 Months. DRINC scores were correlated with recent quantity/ frequency of drinking at .37 for Ever and .47 for Past 3 Months. Based on initial studies using this instrument (including NIAAA's Project MATCH), it will be modified to improve its reliability, validity, and utility.

A proper current citation, pending formal publication of the instrument, is:

> Miller, W.R. "The Drinker Inventory of Consequences." Unpublished manuscript, University of New Mexico.

The DRINC is available for use and can be obtained from William R. Miller, Ph.D., Department of Psychology, University of New Mexico, Albuquerque, NM 87131.

MacAndrew Scale

The MacAndrew Scale is a subscale of the original Minnesota Multiphasic Personality Inventory. It is described in the following article:

> MacAndrew, C. The differentiation of male alcoholic outpatients from nonalcoholic psychiatric outpatients by means of the MMPI. *Quarterly Journal of Studies on Alcohol* 26:238–246, 1965.

Addiction Severity Index

The Addiction Severity Index is a research instrument under ongoing development. For information regarding the current version, contact Dr. A. Thomas McLellan, VA Medical Center (116), Philadelphia, PA 19104.

AUDIT

The Alcohol Use Disorders Identification Test was developed for a large collaborative study of brief intervention conducted by the World Health Organization (Babor and Grant 1989; Saunders et al. in press).

References

Appel, C.-P., and Miller, W.R. "The Self-Evaluation of Drinking." Unpublished assessment instrument, University of New Mexico, 1984.

Babor, T.F., and Grant, M. From clinical research to secondary prevention: International collaboration in the development of the Alcohol Use Disorders Identification Test (AUDIT). *Alcohol Health & Research World* 13:371–374, 1989.

Bien, T.H., and Miller, W.R. Brief interventions for alcohol problems: A review. Submitted.

Brown, S.A. Reinforcement expectancies and alcoholism treatment outcome after a one-year follow-up. *Journal of Studies on Alcohol* 46:304–308, 1985.

Brown, J.M., and Miller, W.R. Impact of motivational interviewing on participation and outcome in residential alcoholism treatment. Submitted.

Cacciola, J.; Griffith, J.; and McLellan, A.T. *Addiction Severity Index Instruction Manual.* 4th ed. Philadelphia, PA: Veterans Administration Medical Center, 1987.

DiClemente, C.C., and Hughes, S.O. Stages of change profiles in alcoholism treatment. *Journal of Substance Abuse* 2(2):217–235, 1990.

Hall, S.M.; Havassy, B.E.; and Wasserman, D.A. Commitment to abstinence and acute stress in relapse to alcohol opiates and nicotine. *Journal of Counseling and Clinical Psychology* 58:175–181, 1990.

Horn, J.R.; Wanberg, K.W.; and Foster, F.M. *Guide to the Alcohol Use Inventory.* Minneapolis, MN: National Computer Systems, 1987.

Jacobson, G.R. A comprehensive approach to pretreatment evaluation: I. Detection, assessment, and diagnosis of alcoholism. In: Hester, R.K., and Miller, W.R., eds. *Handbook of Alcoholism Treatment Approaches.* New York: Pergamon Press, 1989. pp. 17–53.

Lezak, M.D. *Neuropsychological Assessment.* 2nd ed. New York: Oxford University Press, 1983.

Markham, M.R.; Miller, W.R.; and Arciniega, L. BACCuS 2.01: Computer software for quantifying alcohol consumption. Submitted. Software available from William R. Miller, Ph.D., Department of Psychology, University of New Mexico, Albuquerque, NM 87131–1161, USA.

Miller, W.R. Alcoholism scales and objective assessment methods: A review. *Psychological Bulletin* 83:649–674, 1976.

Miller, W.R. "The Stages of Change Readiness and Treatment Eagerness Scale (version 5)." Unpublished assessment instrument, University of New Mexico. Available from William R. Miller, Ph.D., Department of Psychology, University of New Mexico, Albuquerque, NM 87131–1161, USA.

Miller, W.R.; Heather, N.; and Hall, W. Calculating standard drink units: International comparisons. *British Journal of Addictions* 86:43–47, 1991.

Miller, W.R., and Marlatt, G.A. *Manual for the Comprehensive Drinker Profile.* Odessa, FL: Psychological Assessment Resources, 1984.

Miller, W.R., and Marlatt, G.A. *Manual Supplement for the Brief Drinker Profile, Follow-Up Drinker Profile, and Collateral Interview Form.* Odessa, FL: Psychological Assessment Resources, 1987.

Miller, W.R., and Saucedo, C.F. Assessment of neuropsychological impairment and brain damage in problem drinkers. In: Golden, C.J.: Moses, J.A., Jr.; Coffman, J.A.; Miller, W.R.; and Strider, F.D., eds. *Clinical Neuropsychology: Interface With Neurologic and Psychiatric Disorders.* New York: Grune & Stratton, 1983.

Miller, W.R., and Sovereign, R.G. The check-up: A model for early intervention in addictive behaviors. In: Løberg, T.; Miller, W.R.; Nathan, P.E.; and Marlatt, G.A., eds. *Addictive Behaviors: Prevention and Early Intervention.* Amsterdam: Swets and Zeitlinger, 1989. pp. 219-231.

Miller, W.R.; Sovereign, R.G.; and Krege, B. Motivational interviewing with problem drinkers: II. The Drinker's Check-up as a preventive intervention. *Behavioural Psychotherapy* 16:251–268,1988.

Prochaska, J.O., and DiClemente, C.C. *The Transtheoretical Approach: Crossing Traditional Boundaries of Therapy.* Homewood, IL: Dow Jones, Irwin, 1984.

Prochaska, J.O., and DiClemente, C.C. Stages of change in the modification of problem behavior. In: Hersen, M.; Eisler, R.; and Miller, P.M. *Progress in Behavior Modification.* Vol. 28. Sycamore, IL: Sycamore Publishing, 1992.

Saunders, J.B.; Aasland, O.G.; Babor, T.F.; de la Fuente, J.R.; and Grant, M. WHO collaborative project on early detection of persons with harmful alcohol consumption. II. Development of the screening instrument "AUDIT." *British Journal of Addiction,* in press.

Selzer, M.L. The Michigan Alcoholism Screening Test: The quest for a new diagnostic instrument. *American Journal of Psychiatry* 127:89–94, 1971.

Skinner, H.A., and Horn, J.L. *Alcohol Dependence Scale (ADS) User's Guide.* Toronto, Ontario: Addiction Research Foundation, 1984.

Sobell, M.B.; Maisto, S.A.; Sobell, L.C.; Cooper, A.M.; Cooper, T.; and Sanders, B. Developing a prototype for evaluating alcohol treatment effectiveness. In Sobell, L.C.; Sobell, M.B.; and Ward, E., eds. *Evaluating Alcohol and Drug Treatment Effectiveness: Recent Advances.* New York: Pergamon Press, 1980. pp. 129–150.

Handouts for Clients

Personal Feedback Report Form

This form is used in Project MATCH to summarize information obtained from the pretreatment assessment battery and is discussed with and given to the client in the early sessions of MET. It is an example of the type of form that may be adapted for use in other reseach studies involving MET.

Understanding Your Personal Feedback Report

Project MATCH clients receive a copy of this material to take home with them to read in conjunction with their PFR. It summarizes important information that helps the client understand the implications of their scores on the assessment instruments. Again, it is an example of the Project MATCH material that may be adapted for use in other research studies involving MET.

"Alcohol and You"

This pamplet was developed by Dr. William R. Miller and is suitable for duplication and distribution to clients.

PERSONAL FEEDBACK REPORT

Location _____.

Name: _____ ID_____.

1. YOUR DRINKING _____

Number of standard "drinks" per week: _____ drinks

Your drinking relative to American adults (same sex): _____ percentile

2. LEVEL OF INTOXICATION _____

Estimated Blood Alcohol Concentration (BAC) peaks:

in a typical week: _____ mg %

on a heavier day of drinking: _____ mg (Y0

3. RISK FACTORS _____

Tolerance Level:

_____Low (0-60)   _____Medium (61-120)   _____High (121-180)   _____Very High (181+)

Other Drug Risk:

_____Low   _____Medium   _____High

Family Risk:_____

Low: 0-1   Medium: 2-3   High: 4-6   Very High: 7 +

MacAndrew Score:_____

Normal Range: 0-23   Medium Risk: 24-29   High Risk: 30 +

Age at onset:_____**years**

Under 25 - Higher Risk   25 - 39 Medium Risk   40 + Lower Risk

4. NEGATIVE CONSEQUENCES _____

Severity of Problems

	Low	Medium	High	Very High
AUDIT	0-7	8-15	16-25	26-40

Your Score: _____

DRINC: Ever happened	Low	Medium	High	Very High
	55-60	61-75	76-90	91 +

Your Score: _____

(Additional information on attached sheet.)

5. BLOOD TESTS _____

SGOT (AST): _____ Normal range: 5-35

GGTP (GGT): _____ Normal range: 0-30 Low Normal

31-50 High Normal

51 + Elevated / Abnormal

SGPT (ALT): _____ Normal range: 7-56

Uric Acid: _____ Normal range: 2.6-5.6

Bilirubin: _____ Normal range: .2-1.2

6. NEUROPSYCHOLOGICAL TESTS _____

SV	Well Above Average 1	Above Average 2	Average 3	Below Average 4	Well Below Average 5
TMTA	1	2	3	4	5
TMTB	1	2	3	4	5
SYDM	1	2	3	4	5
SHVA	1	2	3	4	5

Therapist: _____

Understanding Your Personal Feedback Report

The Personal Feedback Report summarizes results from your pre-treatment evaluation. Your therapist has explained these to you. This information is to help you understand the written report you have received and to remember what your therapist told you.

Your report consists of two sheets. The first sheet provides information from your pretreatment interviews. Attached to this is a second sheet summarizing your answers to a questionnaire, the Alcohol Use Inventory. The following information is presented section by section to help you understand what your results mean.

1. Your Drinking

The first line in this section shows the number of drinks that you reported having in a typical drinking week. Because different alcohol beverages vary in their strength, we have converted your regular drinking pattern into standard "one drink" units. In this system, one drink is equal to:

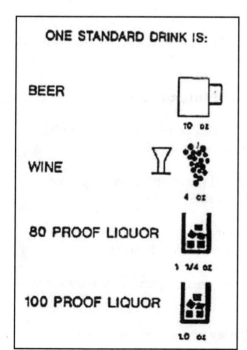

ONE STANDARD DRINK IS:

BEER — 10 oz

WINE — 4 oz

80 PROOF LIQUOR — 1 1/4 oz

100 PROOF LIQUOR — 1.0 oz

10 ounces of beer	(5 percent alcohol)	or
4 ounces of table wine	(12 percent alcohol)	or
2.5 ounces of fortified wine (sherry, port, etc.)	(20 percent alcohol)	or
1.25 ounces of 80 proof liquor	(40 percent alcohol)	or
1 ounce of 100 proof liquor	(50 percent alcohol)	

All of these drinks contain the same amount of the same kind of alcohol: one-half ounce of pure ethyl alcohol.

This first piece of information, then, tells you how many of these standard drinks you have been consuming per week of drinking, according to what you reported in your interview. (If you have not been drinking for a period of time recently, this refers to your pattern of drinking before you stopped.)

To give you an idea of how this compares with the drinking of American adults in general, the second number in section 1 is a *percentile* figure. This tells you what percentage of U.S. men (if you are a man) or women (if you are a woman) drink less than you reported drinking in a typical week of drinking. If this number were 60, for example, it would mean that your drinking is higher than 60 percent of Americans of your sex (or that 40 percent drink as much as you reported, or more).

How much is too much? It depends on many factors. Current research indicates that people who average three or more standard drinks per day have much higher risk of health and social problems. For some people, however, even 1–2 drinks per day would be too many. Pregnant women, for example, are best advised to abstain from alcohol altogether, because even small amounts of regular drinking have been found to increase risk for the unborn child. Certain health problems (such as liver disease) make even moderate drinking unsafe. Some people find that they are unable to drink moderately, and having even one or two drinks leads to intoxication.

Your total number of drinks per week tells only part of the story. It is not healthy, for example, to have 12 drinks per week by saving them all up for Saturdays. Neither is it safe to have even a few drinks and then drive. This raises the important question of level of intoxication.

2. Level of Intoxication

A second way of looking at your past drinking is to ask what level of intoxication you have been reaching. It is possible to estimate the amount of alcohol that would be circulating in your bloodstream, based on the pattern of drinking your reported. Blood alcohol concentration (BAC) is an important indication of the extent to which alcohol would be affecting your body and behavior. It is used by police and the courts, for example, to determine whether a driver is too impaired to operate a motor vehicle.

To understand better what BAC means, consider the list of common effects of different levels of intoxication.

Common Effects of Different Levels of Intoxication

20–60 mg%	This is the "normal" social drinking range. NOTE: Driving, even at these levels, is unsafe.
80 mg%	Memory, judgment, and perception are impaired. Legally intoxicated in some States.
100 mg%	Reaction time and coordination of movement are affected. Legally intoxicated in all States.
150 mg%	Vomiting may occur in normal drinkers; balance is often impaired.
200 mg%	Memory "blackout" may occur, causing loss of recall for events occurring while intoxicated.

300 mg%   Unconsciousness in a normal person, though some remain conscious at levels in excess of 600 mg% if tolerance is very high.

400–500 mg%   Fatal dose for a normal person, though some survive higher levels if tolerance is very high.

The two figures shown in section 2 are computer-calculated estimates of your highest (peak) BAC level during a typical week of drinking and during one of your heaviest days of drinking.

It is important to realize that there is no known "safe" level of intoxication when driving or engaging in other potentially hazardous activities (such as swimming, boating, hunting, and operating tools or machinery). Blood alcohol levels as low as 40–60 mg% can decrease crucial abilities. Adding to the danger, drinkers typically do not realize that they are impaired. The only safe BAC when driving is *zero*. If you must drive after drinking, plan to allow enough time for all of the alcohol to be eliminated from your body before driving. The tables below can be helpful in determining how long it takes to eliminate alcohol completely:

Approximate hours from first drink to zero alcohol concentration levels for men

		Your weight in pounds							
		120	140	160	180	200	220	240	260
	1	2	2	2	1.5	1	1	1	1
Number	**2**	4	3.5	3	3	2.5	2	2	2
of	**3**	6	5	4.5	4	3.5	3.5	3	3
Drinks	**4**	8	7	6	5.5	5	4.5	4	3.5
	5	10	8.5	7.5	6.5	6	5.5	5	4.5

One drink = 10 oz of beer or 4 oz of wine or 1 oz of liquor (100 proof)

Approximate hours from first drink to zero alcohol concentration levels for women

		Your weight in pounds							
		120	140	160	180	200	220	240	260
	1	3	2.5	2	2	2	1.5	1.5	1
Number	**2**	6	5	4	4	3.5	3	3	2.5
of	**3**	9	7.5	6.5	5.5	5	4.5	4	4
Drinks	**4**	12	9.5	8.5	7.5	6.5	6	5.5	5
	5	15	12	10.5	9.5	8	7.5	7	6

3. Risk Factors

It is clear that some people have a much higher risk of alcohol and other drug problems. This section provides you with some information about your own level of risk, based on your personal characteristics. "High risk" does not mean that one will definitely have serious problems with alcohol or other drugs. Neither does "low risk" mean that one will be free of such problems. High-risk people, however, have greater chances of developing serious problems.

Tolerance

Your peak BAC levels, given in section 2, are one reasonably good reflection of your level of tolerance for alcohol. If you are reaching BAC levels beyond the normal social drinking range (especially if you are not feeling some of the normal effects of lower BACs), it means that you have a higher tolerance for alcohol. This is partly hereditary and partly the result of changes in the body that occur with heavier drinking Some people are proud of this tolerance—the ability "to hold your liquor"—and think it means they are not being harmed by alcohol. Actually, the opposite is true. Tolerance for alcohol may be a serious *risk factor* for alcohol problems. The person with a high tolerance for alcohol reaches high BAC levels, which can damage the brain and other organs of the body but has *no built-in warning* that it is happening. Tolerance is not a protection against being harmed by drinking; to the contrary, it makes damage more likely because of the false confidence that it encourages. It is a bit like a person who has no sense of pain. Pain is an important warning signal. People who feel no pain can seriously injure themselves without realizing it. It is the same with people who have a high tolerance for alcohol.

Many people believe that tolerance ("holding your liquor") means that a person gets rid of alcohol at a faster rate than others. Although people do differ in how quickly their bodies can clear alcohol, tolerance has more to do with actually being at a high blood alcohol level and not feeling it.

Other Drug Use

A person who uses other drugs besides alcohol runs several additional risks. Decreased use of one drug may simply result in the increased use of another. The effects of different drugs can multiply when they are taken together, with dangerous results. A tolerance to one drug can increase tolerance to another, and it is common for multiple drug users to become addicted to several drugs. The use of other drugs, then, increases your risk for serious problems. Based on the lifetime drug use that you reported during your interview, your risk in this regard was judged to be low, medium, or high.

Family Risk

People who have a family history of alcohol or other drug problems among their blood relatives clearly are at higher risk themselves. The exact reason for this higher risk is unknown, but it appears that the risk is inherited to an important extent. People may inherit a higher tolerance for alcohol or a body that is particularly sensitive to alcohol in certain ways. In any event, a family history of alcohol problems increases personal risk.

Personality Pattern

Although there is no single personality style associated with alcohol and drug problems, certain patterns are linked to higher risk. One questionnaire you completed—the MacAndrew Scale—measures this particular kind of risk. People who score higher on this scale as teenagers, for example, have been found to have higher risk for developing serious problems with alcohol in adulthood.

Age at Onset

Recent research indicates that the younger a person is when drinking problems start, the greater the person's risk for developing serious consequences and dependence. Although serious problems can occur at any time of life, a younger beginning does represent a significant risk factor.

4. Negative Consequences

From your pretreatment interview, two scores were calculated to reflect the current overall severity of your negative consequences from drinking.

AUDIT

The AUDIT is a scale devised by the World Health Organization to evaluate a person's problematic involvement with alcohol. Higher scores reflect recent problems related to drinking.

DRINC

Another way to look at risks and effects of drinking is to add up alcohol's negative effects throughout one's lifetime. Your score on this scale reflects the extent to which your drinking has had negative effects over the course of your life thus far. The higher your score, the more harm has resulted from your drinking.

5. Blood Tests

Your pretreatment evaluation also included a blood sample. These particular blood tests were chosen because they have been shown in previous research to be negatively affected by heavy drinking. You should realize that normal results on these tests do not guarantee that you are in good health (for example, that your liver is functioning completely normally). An abnormal score on one or more of these test however, probably reflects unhealthy changes in your body resulting from excessive use of alcohol and/or other drugs.

Research indicates that modestly abnormal scores on the blood tests reported here will often show improvement and a return to normal range when harmful drinking and other drug use patterns are changed. The longer one continues drinking, however, the more difficult it is to reverse the physical damage.

These tests are directly related to how the liver is working. Your liver is extremely important to your health. It is involved in producing energy, and it filters and neutralizes impurities and poisons in your bloodstream. Alcohol damages the liver, and after a long period of heavy drinking, parts of the liver begin to die. This is the process of cirrhosis, but physical changes in the liver can be caused by drinking long before cirrhosis appears. As the liver becomes damaged, it begins to leak enzymes into the blood and is less efficient in doing its work. This can be reflected in abnormally elevated values on the tests reported in this section.

Elevated values on any of these tests should be taken seriously. They do not happen by chance and are very likely related to physical changes in the body caused by excessive drinking. Consult a physician who is knowledgeable about the effects of alcohol on the body.

6. Neuro-psychological Tests

Some of the earliest damaging effects of drinking may be seen in certain types of abilities that are affected by alcohol. Certain patterns of brain impairment have been shown to be especially related to heavy drinking. The brain is very vulnerable to alcohol, and over a long span of time, a substantial amount of damage can occur in a heavy drinker. (Brain impairment from the use of certain other drugs has also been shown.)

Such damage occurs gradually. In later stages, it can be seen in x-rays of the brain, which show actual shrinkage and other changes in shape and density. Long before this occurs, however, harmful changes in brain functioning can be measured by psychological tests, several of which you completed. Research indicates that such negative effects can often be reversed, sometimes completely, if the individual stops or reduces drinking.

The four tests included in section 6 have been found to be related to heavy drinking. For comparison purposes, we include one test (SV) that is not usually affected by drinking to give you an idea of where your scores might normally be expected to fall. People who are heavy drinkers tend to score more poorly (higher) on the four alcohol-sensitive tests (TMTA, TMTB, SYDM, and SHVA) than on SV.

A high score on any one scale is not necessarily reason for concern. There are many reasons why a single score might be elevated. A *pattern* of elevated scores, however, resembles the kinds of problems that emerge among excessive drinkers. Studies of individuals currently in treatment for alcohol problems consistently show impairment on these measures.

Alcohol's effects on the brain have sometimes been described as "premature aging." The abnormal changes in the brain of a heavy drinker do resemble normal changes that occur with advanced age. For this reason, your scores reflected above take into account your present age. Scores of 4 or 5 represent below-average performance relative to others in your age group.

The Alcohol Use Inventory

You completed a longer questionnaire that asked in detail about your drinking. This questionnaire has been given to thousands of people seeking treatment for alcohol problems. Based on your answers, 24 scores were obtained, and these are shown on the Alcohol Use Inventory Profile section of your Personal Feedback Report.

Notice that each score falls into one of three ranges. The *white* range indicates a low score, the *light grey* range is for medium scores, and the *dark grey* range reflects high scores—*compared to other people in treatment for alcohol problems.* If, for example, your score for the "Quantity" scale (#13) was in the medium (light grey) range, it would mean that you drink about an average amount *for people already receiving treatment for alcohol problems.* This would be far above the average amount of drinking for Americans in general.

Here are brief reminders of what each scale means. If you want to discuss your results in more detail, contact your therapist.

Benefits

The first four scales reflect possible *reasons* for excessive drinking. A high score on one of these scales may indicate a way in which you have come to depend on alcohol. In order to be free of alcohol problems, it would be important to find other ways of dealing with these areas of your life.

Social Improvement Drinking

People who score in the medium or high range on this scale tend to be social drinkers. They may use alcohol to relax and feel more comfortable around others, to be friendly, or to enjoy social events more. They might have difficulty knowing how to handle their social lives without alcohol.

Mental Improvement Drinking

Those who score medium or high on this scale tend to like the way alcohol changes their *thinking* or *mental state*. They indicate that when they drink they feel more creative or alert, work better, or see the world in more enjoyable ways.

Managing Mood With Drinking

On this scale, medium or high scores indicate people who use alcohol to change how they feel. They drink to forget, to feel less anxious or depressed, or to escape from unpleasant moods. Without alcohol, they might experience difficulty coping with their own emotions.

Marital Coping by Drinking

(If you are not married, you will have no score here.) People who score in the medium or high range on this scale report that they drink because of problems in their marriage.

Styles of Drinking

The next three scales reflect different *styles* of using alcohol. Low scores on these scales describe a different style of drinking but do not mean that there are no problems.

Gregarious Drinking

A medium or high score indicates a preference for drinking around other people. Those who prefer to drink alone score low on this scale.

Compulsive Drinking

Medium and high scores on scale 6 indicate a close attachment to alcohol. Such people tend to think about alcohol a lot, keep a supply handy, and drink in a "compulsive," predictable style.

Sustained Drinking

People who score in the medium and high range on this scale tend to be regular, steady drinkers, drinking every day or most days. Those who score lower on this scale are not such steady drinkers but have periods of drinking and nondrinking.

Consequences

Scales 8–12 reflect possible negative consequences of drinking. Higher scores on these scales reflect more problems, *compared with people already in treatment for alcohol problems*. Thus, a person with a lower score may still have some problems but fewer than most people now in treatment for alcohol problems.

Loss of Control

One kind of difficulty that people can have is that they lose control of themselves when drinking. They get into trouble, arguments, or fights. They may do embarrassing things or hurt themselves or other people. They may not remember things that happened while drinking (blackouts) or may drink until they become unconscious. Medium and high scores indicate these kinds of problems.

Role Problems

Drinking can also cause social difficulties, 'such as problems at work or school, and conflicts with the law. Medium and high scores indicate that alcohol is seriously interfering with social functioning.

Delirium

If people continue to drink heavily over a period of time, they may develop a pattern of physical *dependence* on alcohol. A number of changes occur, usually gradually, that make it more difficult for a person to live without alcohol. This can include actual addiction to alcohol, so that the person becomes uncomfortable or even ill when stopping or cutting down drinking. Medium to high scores on this scale reflect some of the more serious signs of addiction to alcohol. For example, stopping drinking can result in hallucinations (seeing, hearing, or feeling things that are not really there) or fuzzy thinking.

Hangover

Hangovers are actually a form of alcohol withdrawal, the body's "rebound" reaction to alcohol. Medium or high scores on scale 11 reflect some of these signs of addiction to alcohol: feeling shaky or sick to the stomach, feeling your heart racing, having a seizure, or feeling hot or cold flashes when sobering up.

Marital Problems

People who score in the medium or high range of scale 12 report that they are having problems in their marriage because of their drinking (If you are not married, this scale will be blank.)

Personal Concern

How much do you recognize and acknowledge problems with drinking? This is what scales 13–17 describe.

Quantity of Drinking

Scale 13 is a rough indicator of the *amount* you said you have been drinking. (Section 1 of your Personal Feedback Report is a more accurate indication.) Remember that this is in comparison to other people seeking treatment for alcohol problems.

Guilt/Worry

To what extent have you felt guilty about your drinking or worried about what it is doing to you and those around you? Medium and high scores reflect more of this kind of concern.

Help Before

To what extent have you sought help for your drinking before coming to this program? The more things you have tried before, the higher this score will be.

Receptiveness

To what extent do you feel ready and willing to receive help for your drinking? Medium and high scores reflect greater willingness to accept help.

Awareness

To what extent are you aware of problems being caused by your drinking? Medium and high scores indicate recognition of more serious problems.

Second Order Scales

Scores A through F are summaries. They do not contain new information but rather combine information from scales 1–17. Nevertheless, they are useful as overall problem indicators.

Enhancement Drinking

Medium and high scores on this scale reflect drinking to cope, to enhance your life, or to get what you perceive to be the benefits of drinking. To the extent that this score is high, there would be some challenges to face in changing your drinking, because you have relied on alcohol for these purposes. Scales 1–5 show you where you may have relied most on alcohol to enhance your life.

Obsessive Drinking

Medium and high scores on this scale indicate what are often thought of as classic "alcoholic" drinking patterns. The drinking of high scorers on this scale tends to be steady and "driven," occupying much of the person's time and energy. High scorers think about drinking quite a bit and will go to considerable lengths to make sure they can drink. It has become a central part of their lives.

Disruption

Both of these two scales report the extent to which life has been disrupted by drinking. Medium and high scores indicate serious symptoms and problems resulting from drinking.

Anxious Concern

Medium and high scores on this scale indicate worry, anxiety, or concern about drinking, as well as alcohol's negative effects on the person's emotional life.

Recognition and Awareness

Medium and high scores here indicate a recognition of a need for change in drinking and/or willingness to get help with drinking.

General

Finally, the Alcohol Involvement Scale is one general indicator of the overall severity of alcohol problems. The higher this score, the more serious and severe the alcohol problems. Remember that scores are low, medium, or high in relation to people already in treatment for alcohol problems.

Summary

Your Personal Feedback Report summarizes a large amount of information that you provided during your pretreatment interviews. Sometimes this information can seem surprising or even discouraging. The best use of feedback like this is to consider it as you decide what, if anything, you will do about your drinking. Many of the kinds of problems covered in your Personal Feedback Report do improve when heavy drinking is stopped. What you do with this information is up to you. Your report is designed to give you a clear picture of where you are at present so that you can make good decisions about where you want to go from here.

Alcohol And You

William R. Miller, Ph.D.

Have you ever wondered:

Whether you drink too much?
Whether alcohol is harming you or putting you at risk?
How heavy drinking affects your health?
How much is too much?

■

Drinking

Drinking alcohol is certainly common in our society. About two-thirds of American adults have a drink at least occasionally, while the other one-third don't drink at all. Of those who do drink, the vast majority use alcohol very moderately, and will never have serious problems with it. For them, alcohol beverages are simply that: *beverages* to be enjoyed now and then as part of a meal or a social occasion.

Yet it is important to remember that alcohol is also a *drug*, and a potentially dangerous one. People who use it beyond moderate levels have a much greater risk for a wide variety of illnesses and problems. Overdrinking results in up to 200,000 deaths each year in the United States alone — about 550 every day —and many more people than that are ill or injured because of their drinking.

Drinking is such a serious health problem in our country, in part, because many people who drink too much don't think of themselves as problem drinkers, or even heavy drinkers. They see themselves as normal, moderate drinkers. Although they may realize that their drinking has negative consequences now and then, they also enjoy drinking, and aren't sure they need to make a change. Heavy drinking can seem quite normal if one has friends who drink just as much, or even more.

This booklet explains some of the risks associated with heavy drinking, based on current scientific knowledge. Of course no one person will experience all, or even most of the risks and problems discussed here. Some are relatively rare, while others happen to many people who drink too much.

The point is that it is important to know about alcohol, just as a doctor or pharmacist informs you about the effects of drugs that are prescribed. When you know the facts, you can make better choices. What you decide to do with this information, of course, is up to you.

Heavy Drinking

How much is too much? It is difficult to say exactly. Studies suggest that people who have no more than 1 or 2 drinks per day have no higher risk in general than non-drinkers. ("One drink" here means a 10-ounce glass of beer, or a 4-ounce glass of wine, or one ounce of 100 proof spirits.) Only 8% of American adults (and only 4% of women) average 3 drinks or more per day, and those who do so suffer many more diseases, injuries, and problems than do light drinkers or nondrinkers.

Surprisingly few Americans are aware of the risks of heavier drinking. Most know that drunk driving is dangerous, and that alcoholics may get liver disease. Yet few really understand how many areas of life and health can be harmed by alcohol, and how quickly and easily this can happen. Over time, heavy drinking can damage one's relationships, job, intelligence, and emotional and physical health. Often the damage is gradual, occurring slowly over a period of years, so that one may not even notice that it is happening. Other kinds of alcohol-related damage and problems happen suddenly.

What kinds of problems can happen because of overdrinking? Health risks will be considered first; then social and psychological risks will be discussed.

Health Risks

Heart and Fitness

Is alcohol good for the heart? Although light drinkers (no more than 1-2 drinks per day) seem to be at least as healthy as abstainers, heavier drinkers can do serious damage to their health and fitness. Alcohol weakens heart muscle, decreasing cardiovascular fitness, and heavy drinkers have much higher risk of heart disease. Heavy drinking also increases blood pressure, and can contribute to hypertension. The electrical control patterns of the heart can be disrupted by an episode of heavy drinking, which can cause the heart to race or skip beats, even in young people with no previous history of heart disease.

The Brain and Nervous System

The human brain is sometimes the first organ to be damaged by heavy drinking. Alcohol kills nerve cells, and many heavy drinkers show evidence of brain damage. If this process continues for a period of years, the brain literally shrinks in size, due to the destruction of so many brain cells. Such shrinkage can be observed (by special X-rays known as a "CAT scan") in about half of people in treatment for alcohol problems.

It is not surprising, then, that heavy drinkers also show significant decreases in their mental abilities. Alcohol damages the ability to learn and remember new material, to think abstractly, and to adjust flexibly to changes. One recent study found a strong relationship between amount of drinking and grades in college students: the more they drank, the lower their grade point average. After years of heavy drinking, a disease known as Wernicke-Korsakoff syndrome can occur, permanently damaging the person's ability to remember things from one day to the next. The damaging effects of alcohol have been likened to a premature aging of the brain. The mental abilities of a 30-year-old heavy drinker may resemble those of an 80-year-old nondrinker.

Nerve cells outside the brain are also damaged by heavy drinking. Usually the first effects are experienced in the legs and feet, or arms and hands. The signs include muscle weakness, pain, tingling, or numbness. These result from "peripheral neuropathy," the dying off of nerve channels that serve the legs and arms.

The good news is that the nervous system, including the brain, can repair itself to some extent if a heavy drinker stops drinking. Although once dead, brain cells are not replaced, the brain has a remarkable ability to make new connections, and former drinkers often show significant improvement in their mental abilities during their first year or so without alcohol.

The Digestive System

Alcohol can irritate and damage the sensitive tissue of the digestive system. Perhaps the most direct experience of this is to take a drink of straight liquor. It burns — all the way down. It irritates the lining of the lips, mouth, throat and stomach. Alcohol also releases digestive acid in the stomach, which adds to the irritating effect of the alcohol itself. Heavy drinkers experience higher rates of gastritis, ulcers, and bleeding of the digestive system. Pancreatitis, an extremely painful and sometimes fatal inflammation of the pancreas, also occurs at higher rates in heavy drinkers.

Cancers of the digestive system are much more common in heavy drinkers — some occurring at more than 40 times the normal rate. Heavy drinkers account for a majority of head and neck cancers: those in the mouth, tongue, throat, and esophagus.

Because alcohol contains a high level of empty calories —those with no nutritional value — heavy drinkers also tend not to eat properly. They may drink up to half of their daily calories. This can result in both weight gain and nutritional deficits. To make matters worse, alcohol prevents the body from fully absorbing and using even those vitamins and other nutrients that are available.

The Liver

The liver is the body's main defense against poisons and impurities in the blood. It is also important in manufacturing energy for the whole body, including the brain, muscles, and heart. Because alcohol is a toxic chemical, it is the liver's job to remove it from the bloodstream. When alcohol is present, the liver gives priority to getting rid of it, and in the process does not perform some of its normal work, such as getting rid of fats and body waste products.

As a result, heavy drinkers tend to pile up fat in the liver and bloodstream. The liver itself becomes fatty and enlarges, contributing to the "beer belly" appearance.

Social and Psychological Problems

The damaging physical effects of heavy drinking are only part of the picture. Heavy drinkers are also at risk for many other kinds of problems.

Risk-Taking and Accidents

Alcohol-related accidents and violence are the leading cause of death among Americans under the age of 35. How can this be?

There are several reasons. First, as many people know, drinking makes a person less in control. Alcohol, even at levels well under the "legal limit" can cause dangerous changes in a person's ability to react, to control muscles, and to perceive the world accurately.

These changes are made all the more dangerous by something else that happens when a person drinks. Among the first things to be changed by alcohol is a person's *judgment*. Experienced race drivers, for example, become much poorer drivers after even a few drinks, but may actually perceive themselves to be better drivers under the influence of alcohol. In short, a person cannot tell how much he or she is being affected. You can't judge when your judgment is affected!

These judgment changes, in turn, often make a person overconfident, and more likely to take foolish risks. After a few drinks, people are less able to make good decisions, and are more likely to do things they would never do while sober. Sometimes the result is only embarrassment, but other times it is much more serious. A majority of people in prison, for example, committed their crimes while under the influence of alcohol. When drinking, people are more likely to misjudge others as threatening or challenging them, and to react impulsively, aggressively, even violently. Other misjudgments can be disastrous as well. Tens of thousands of deaths and hundreds of thousands of injuries happen each year because people drink before driving vehicles, using power tools or firearms, or engaging in fun but hazardous sports such as swimming, boating, or skiing — activities where even a small misjudgment can be very dangerous.

Mood

Drinking also affects mood. After one or two drinks, some people feel happier, more relaxed, less tense and anxious. Interestingly, these same changes happen when people believe they are drinking alcohol, even if they are not. Alcohol itself is a depressant drug, and its effects, in heavier doses at least, are to turn good feelings bad, and to make bad feelings worse. After several drinks, mood tends to take a turn for the worse. It is around this same

This condition is reversible, but if the heavy drinking continues a different kind of damage occurs. Liver cells begin to die off, and are replaced by scar tissue. The beginnings of this irreversible process can be seen long before it reaches the disease stage known as cirrhosis. As living liver tissue is replaced by scars, the liver is less and less able to produce energy and filter impurities (including alcohol) from the bloodstream.

The Immune System

Alcohol decreases the body's ability to fight off diseases and infections. The immune system — the body's defense — works less efficiently whenever a person drinks, and over a period of heavy drinking the body's defenses can be greatly weakened. As a result, the person becomes more vulnerable to infections, cancers, and other illnesses. The risk of cancers in general among heavy drinkers is twice that of other people. Sores and injuries tend to heal more slowly, and it becomes harder to shake off sickness.

The Reproductive System

Alcohol has clear negative effects on the reproductive system. In men, drinking decreases the body level of testosterone, the primary male hormone. If a man drinks heavily for a period of time, this loss of testosterone can result in a "feminization" of his body — the loss of body hair, enlargement of fatty tissue in the breasts, and a shrinking of the testicles. Heavy drinking can also contribute to sexual problems such as impotence.

In women, heavy drinking has been linked to increased rates of sexual, menstrual and other gynecological problems. Alcohol also changes sex hormone balances in women, and can promote a loss of feminine body characteristics. Heavy drinking during pregnancy has been clearly linked to increased rates of miscarriage and stillbirth, and to birth defects, behavior problems, and mental retardation of children exposed to alcohol in the womb. Alcohol consumed by a pregnant woman directly affects the fetus, and there is no known safe level of drinking during pregnancy.

Summary

In short, once alcohol is consumed, it is rapidly distributed throughout the body, where it affects virtually every organ system. There are no proven beneficial health effects of drinking, but there are many proven harmful effects of heavy drinking. Many of these damaging effects can be reversed, at least partly, when a heavy drinker stops drinking. In general, the longer the period of heavy drinking, the less reversible the damage, but quitting usually results in improved health and fitness, even after many years of excess.

point, however, that alcohol also affects memory, so people tend not to remember the depressing effects of drinking — only the seemingly positive effects of the first drink or two.

Among heavy drinkers, depression is common. There are many possible reasons for this. Yet when heavy drinkers get treatment and quit, usually their depression goes away after a few weeks. Alcohol is not a stimulant or an upper. It is a downer.

Relationships

Heavy drinking can damage close relationships. "You always hurt the one you love" seems to be especially true for people who drink too much. Heavy drinkers have, on average, more problems in their marriages and other relationships, and higher rates of separation and divorce. One's ability to be a good parent can also be harmed by overdrinking, resulting in family problems. Child abuse and neglect are more common among heavy drinking parents.

Problems and Coping

One reason why heavy drinkers' relationships may get into trouble is that the person begins to drink alcohol as a *solution* to problems, as a way of trying to cope. Drinking takes the place of talking and working out difficulties in other ways. It can be a tempting trap. Alcohol dulls memory, and makes the problems seem to go away — at least for the time being.

Yet while people are drinking to ease cares and worries, the troubles aren't really going away. In fact, they often get worse, because the drinker makes little or no attempt to find better ways to handle things. It's just easier to let things go, to take a break, to forget. So things begin to fall apart — sometimes a little at a time, sometimes in bigger shocks — and it happens in different ways for different people:

• Friends pull back or drift away

• Problems start showing up on the job or at school: coming in late, missing days, not working up to your abilities, making more mistakes, missing opportunities, having accidents, putting off responsibilities

• Tension builds up in the family: more complaints, problems, and arguments, less fun and closeness

• Health and fitness begin to be affected

• Money problems increase: too much is spent on alcohol, and on paying for problems or poor decisions related to drinking

Because alcohol can make it hard to see what is really happening, heavy drinkers often feel misunderstood, unfairly treated, harassed, or just unlucky. And as things get worse, the temptation is — to drink.

Personal Risk

Many people drink alcohol moderately without ever experiencing significant problems. Why is it that some people have trouble with alcohol while others do not?

Part of the answer, of course, lies in how much a person drinks. The more one drinks, the greater the risk of suffering the negative health, psychological and social consequences. Yet that is not the whole picture. Certain people have a greater risk than others. Here are a few factors that have been shown to increase a person's danger for overdrinking and running into significant problems with alcohol:

• Having a family history of relatives with alcohol or other drug problems

• Drinking to get drunk

• Being able to "hold your liquor" — seeming to be less affected by alcohol than most people

• Having one or more memory "blackouts" due to drinking

• Drinking to relieve bad feelings or to escape from problems

• Having friends who are heavy drinkers

• Thinking of alcohol as a positive life influence, which helps people be more friendly, happy, relaxed, successful, etc.

• Using other drugs which, when combined with alcohol, increase the effects and dangers of drinking

People with these characteristics seem to have higher risk for the kinds of problems described earlier. A person doesn't have to have any of these in order to be harmed by alcohol, of course. It's just that these are risk factors, which increase one's chances for harm from overdrinking.

Alcohol and You

Probably most of the things mentioned earlier have not happened to you. Even heavier drinkers can sometimes go for many years without piling up too many of these problems. Yet maybe you do see yourself in some of these descriptions, or perhaps you see what might happen to you if your drinking continues as it is.

Is it time for you to make a change? That is your choice. In fact, no one else can decide about your drinking, or change your drinking for you, not even if they want to. To be sure, other people may be able to help quite a bit if you let them, but still in the end it's your decision.

If you want to change your drinking, there are many ways to do it. Some people just decide, and go ahead. Others find that it's easier with some help from friends, professionals, or other people who have been through it. There's no one approach that is best for all. The truth is that there are many different ways, and you keep trying until you find what works for you. If one approach isn't working, try something else. There are books, self-help groups, skilled counselors and psychologists and physicians, spiritual approaches, medications, clinics, and hospitals. There's no one magic answer for everybody, but there are many helpful people and approaches to try.

And in the long run, the chances for change are very good. If you do try to change your drinking and you're like most people, you may not succeed the very first time. It is common to have some setbacks, and it can be tough to make an important change in your life. One try may not do it. Or two, or five. Yet each try brings you closer to getting free, to succeeding in change. Studies show that most people who have problems with alcohol do get better in the long run. For those who decide to do something about their drinking, there is hope.

Prepared for Project MATCH by
The Center on Alcoholism, Substance Abuse, and Addictions (CASAA)
The University of New Mexico, Albuquerque, NM 87131

Appendix B: Motivational Enhancement Therapy in the Aftercare Setting

The manual to this point has focused on the application of the MET model to individuals presenting for treatment at an outpatient facility. The same principles and techniques can be applied effectively in the aftercare clinic. In the aftercare situation, the client has already completed a comprehensive abstinence-oriented inpatient treatment program, and the general focus of treatment will differ. Aftercare clients are more likely to be further along in the change cycle than clients first presenting for treatment. Many of these individuals will have thus far successfully negotiated the precontemplation, contemplation, and determination stages. They will have begun to take action at least in the hospital setting and possibly on several home visits. The real task for these clients is to return to their home environment and successfully sustain their abstinence from alcohol. They will need to transfer learning to be aware of possible pitfalls and remain committed to abstinence in the face of new and challenging situations. Although they can be assumed to be motivated to change if they have spent 14 to 28 days in the hospital, often the hospitalized client is unprepared for the post-hospital environment and the challenge to their motivation that going home will provide.

While the basic principles and techniques of MET remain the same, the overall focus of treatment will be somewhat different. This section briefly outlines variations in the MET sessions when applied to aftercare clients.

Scheduling

Prior to discharge and before the first session, the Project MATCH client will have completed the initial screening, informed consent procedures, and the comprehensive assessment battery. Following completion of the assessment battery and before the client's discharge, project therapists contact the client to introduce themselves and schedule the first aftercare session. Regardless of the details of the particular research protocol being followed, it is desirable to schedule the first session as close as possible to the client's date of discharge.

As noted previously (see "Initial Session"), the therapist stresses the importance of having the spouse or significant other along to the first two sessions and also explains the importance of coming to appointments sober. In the aftercare setting, attempt to have the first appointment immediately prior to discharge so therapist and client will connect before leaving the hospital. This schedule may make spouse attendance problematic without adequate planning

Structuring (see "The Structure of MET Sessions") the therapy sessions is particularly important for aftercare clients. These clients already have completed lengthy inpatient treatment and have well-developed expectations for what therapy sessions should be like. In most cases, these therapy expectations will differ considerably from the nondirective style of MET. Here is an example of what you might say to an aftercare client at the beginning of the first session:

> Before we begin, I'd like to talk a little bit about how we will be working together over the next 3 months. You've already successfully completed the treatment program here, and these aftercare sessions are aimed at helping you maintain the changes that you've begun during your stay in the hospital. Also, we'll be trying to help you deal with new problems that might come up in these first few months following your discharge.

> My approach may be different from what you were used to during your stay in the hospital. For one thing, I'm not going to be *telling* you what you should or shouldn't do. I can help you to think about your present situation or new problems and consider what, if anything, you might want to do, but if there are any decisions to be made or any changing to be done, *you* will be the one doing it. When it comes right down to it, nobody can tell you what to do and certainly nobody can make you change. I'll be giving you a lot of information about yourself, and maybe some advice, but what you do with all of it is completely up to you. I couldn't change you if I wanted to. The only person who can decide whether or how to change is you. How does that sound? (Explore client's and significant other's reactions as previously discussed.)

> Now, you spent a lot of time completing tests and questionnaires for us just before you were discharged. I appreciate the time you spent on those. Today we are going to make good use of the information you gave to us. We'll be going over the results of some of those tests in detail. As you may know, this is the first of four sessions that we will be having. During these sessions, we will take a close look at your situation and help you adjust now that you're out of the hospital. I think you'll find these sessions interesting and helpful.

Reviewing Progress

Since the client has already completed a treatment program and presumably made some commitment for change, it is important to monitor the client's progress in meeting his/her goals. The client's judgment of progress can be assessed with an open-ended question such as, "Well, before we go any further, tell me how things have been going since you came to the hospital?" When asking this question, the therapist may want to look at both the client and the client's SO and allow either one to respond. Allow the client or SO to volunteer information. If the client answers only briefly (e.g., "Oh, fine"), ask for elaboration (e.g., "When you say fine, what do you mean?"). The therapist should use empathic reflection, affirmation, or reframing as discussed previously in responding to the client or SO. If the response of the client or SO does not touch on drinking or urges to drink, it is appropriate to ask direct questions or make statements to elicit this information. As with anything in the MET approach, however, these questions/statements should be asked in a nonjudgmental manner. For example, the statement, "You haven't mentioned anything about your plans for discharge, return to work..." will often prompt a reason.

During the second through the fourth sessions, in response to either reports of drinking or reports of abstinence in the time since discharge, the therapist should attempt to explore the clients' own attributions regarding their behavior. For example, in response to a report of no drinking, the therapist might say, "Well, Joe, it sounds as though you've been doing extremely well. I was wondering what you see yourself doing differently now that's helped you to remain sober?" To the client's response, the therapist should use empathic reflection, affirmation, and reframing as a means of exploring and reinforcing changes the client has made. As noted previously, the goal here is to enhance the attitude of self-responsibility, reinforce effort, and support the client's self-esteem.

In response to a report of drinking since discharge, it is important for the therapist to remain nonjudgmental. At the same time, however, the therapist should explore more carefully the circumstances surrounding the slip or relapse and the client's feelings about it. For example, "Can you tell me more about what was happening at the time you decided to take a drink? How were you feeling?" or "What led up to you deciding to take a drink?" Again, the therapist should use empathic reflection and reframing in discussing the relapse episode. Overall, the therapist should encourage the client to discuss the circumstances leading up to the relapse, the relapse, and how the client felt afterward. The therapist should also explore what the client should do differently in the future to reduce the risk of relapse. For example, "Joe, given this experience you had, what do you think you would do differently in the future to prevent this from happening?" As is basic to the self-motivational approach, the goal here is to allow the client to generate and decide on self-change strategies.

The exploration of relapse situations may lead into several relevant areas of further discussion and exploration. For example, for individuals experiencing considerable guilt over a relapse, the therapist can offer supportive statements and information. "It is not unusual for people to have a slip when they first get out of the hospital. What is important is that they try to evaluate what happened and what changes they need to make to reduce the risk of it happening again. You deserve a lot of credit for catching that slip before it got too far out of hand." Discussion of a relapse episode may also unveil a client's uncertainty over abstinence as their intended goal. In such instances, the therapist should emphasize that while we advise and encourage abstinence as a goal, it is ultimately up to the client to decide (see "Emphasizing Abstinence"). A related issue may be slips in which the client consumes light or moderate levels of alcoholic beverage. In these cases, it is important to reinforce the client's restraint but also, where appropriate, advise the client of the potential risk of even moderate consumption levels. Finally, exploration of relapse situations may reveal considerable resistance (see "Handling Resistance"). It is very important that the therapist not be seen as a judge so the client would be willing to return to talk about the frustrating and embarrassing experience of slipping or relapsing.

Generating Self-Motivational Statements

The discussion of relapses (or abstinence) during the time since discharge provides a gateway into discussing the client's motivation for wanting to change (see "Eliciting Self-Motivational Statements"). For abstinent clients or clients functioning well with respect to drinking, the therapist can elicit the perceived differences they have noted in their life now compared to when they were drinking. This discussion can lead to the client's reviewing reasons for wanting to change. Clients who are doing well sometimes become overconfident, and a review of negative events which occurred before they quit drinking and positive events occurring since quitting can make their initial motivations for change more salient. In most cases, eliciting self-motivational statements from aftercare clients may be easier than eliciting statements from individuals first presenting for treatment.

For individuals who have relapsed, the generation of self-motivational statements is particularly important. In fact, some of these individuals may have reverted to (or never left) the precontemplation or contemplation stage in the cycle of change. Self-motivational statements to bring the client back to the determination and action stages should be elicited (see "Eliciting Self-Motivational Statements").

Providing Personal Feedback

Once the therapist has reviewed the client's progress and elicited self-motivational statements, attention should be turned to giving feedback from the client's predischarge assessment (see "Presenting Personal Feedback"). The personal feedback form and the assessment battery used in Project MATCH is provided in appendix A, with suggestions on how it may be modified to fit the needs of other research protocols. Rather than being abrupt, the therapist should try to make a smooth transition and may want to incorporate feedback with the elicitation of self-motivational statements. For example, in responding to a client's reasons for wanting to quit, the therapist may say, "That's very consistent with what you were telling us on the tests and questionnaires that you completed. Maybe this would be a good time for us to discuss the results of those now." Another transition statement might be, "I think it is important to discuss changes which you think you need to make to prevent a relapse from happening again. In doing that, it might be helpful for us to review the results of the tests and questionnaires you completed just before discharge. This might give you some perspective on where you're at now and maybe what you want to work on."

Feedback for aftercare clients will be similar to that described in previous sections of the manual. Reviewing the level of addiction, quantity/frequency of drinking, patterns of use, and consequences of drinking can be quite helpful in motivating continued commitment to change. Some clients may only now, after several weeks of sobriety, be capable of understanding their destructive pattern of drinking. This information can also be important for helping them develop a solid postdischarge plan. Feedback on family history of drinking and neuropsychological assessments can provide additional information for discussion with client and significant other.

The focus of the feedback with the aftercare client is not so much the need for change as it is the need for continued effort. It would be important to tie in the work and progress the client has made during the hospital stay. In fact, reviewing hospital progress can be a valuable additional topic during the first session of treatment. However, be careful not to get into a discussion that is simply a critique of the hospital or some staff. Encourage them to bring up complaints to the hospital staff if necessary. Keep the focus on the discharge and where do we go from here.

Developing a Plan

With few exceptions, most of the aftercare clients will have already made some commitment for change and have a plan for change. Reviewing this plan in concert with their progress since discharge is important. Once the personal feedback has been provided, the therapist should summarize the main points (see "Summarizing") for the client and elicit the client's perceptions of the information provided (if this has not been done already). For example,

> Just to summarize what we've been talking about, Joe, you indicated that one of your main reasons for seeking treatment was your concern about your health. Certainly, this appeared to be a wise decision since, as we saw, your liver tests were elevated way above normal when you entered the hospital. Your drinking was negatively affecting your liver and could

have led to permanent damage. This is common for individuals with moderate to severe alcohol problems and, as we saw, you seem to fit in this group. We also saw that with abstinence during your time in the hospital your liver tests basically returned to normal. This is very encouraging and indicates that if you remain off alcohol, your health will continue to improve or, at least, not deteriorate further. You also indicated in the tests that one of your most difficult situations with respect to drinking is when you find yourself at home with nothing to do and feeling lonely. This appears to be the problem you ran into last weekend in which you said you had a strong urge to have a drink. You also express some difficulty turning down drinks when you're around some of your old buddies. Based on your discussion here, it certainly sounds like you are committed to staying off alcohol. In fact, since discharge you have been doing extremely well. At this point then, it may be helpful for us to talk about what you feel you need to do or need to continue doing in order to maintain the important change you've already made.

Although it is not necessary to complete the plan for change by the end of the first session, some plan elements should be completed in order to give closure to the first session.

In the second and subsequent sessions, the therapist should complete the plan for change, if it has not been done already. The majority of these sessions will be spent reviewing progress as discussed above, reinforcing the client's change and modifying the plan for change as needed.

The first two sessions of MET are scheduled to occur within a week of each other. Feedback and spouse involvement are scheduled during these sessions. If significant others cannot come in during these sessions, they can be invited to later sessions.

The final two sessions are times when clients can check in and reflect on their progress and problems. If they have lost momentum or have encountered serious problems, this is the time to reflect, empathize, summarize, and offer advice. Followthrough on the plans and modifying plans would be a major focus of these sessions. In Project MATCH, as with the other therapies, ME therapists have available up to two emergency sessions to use if there are crises for the client. These would be used similarly to those in the outpatient condition.

Integrating MET Aftercare With Inpatient Programming

Experiences with Motivational Enhancement Therapy in the aftercare setting have been quite positive. Many patients view the support for *taking personal responsibility* for their aftercare plan to be quite helpful. Although this message may be somewhat at variance with the information given during the inpatient stay, clarification of the MET philosophy and perspective can be an important first step to engaging the patient. The focus on discharge and life after hospitalization is critical for the aftercare patient. Focus not only on the plans for sobriety, which may have been heavily influenced by inpatient staff and other patients, but also on plans for establishing routines and goals postdischarge. Several key issues can arise in this context.

The Prepackaged Plan

Most aftercare patients will have a postdischarge plan that is developed during the hospital program. At times, these plans are rather standardized, depending on the type of inpatient program, and can include AA, group therapy, or disulfiram. They often include messages about employment, relationships, leisure, exercise, and a variety of other activities or life situations. *Exploring this plan* is a critical first step in assisting clients in developing their own unique plan to which they can commit. It is important to explore which elements the clients really believe will work and will fit with their unique situation. *Be careful to have clients be as specific as possible in discussing the plan.* Elicit the details of the plan and how it will work.

In some cases, the discharge plan may not be well formulated or may change as the client leaves the hospital. It is important to *check with the client about how the plans are developing.* From one week to the next, the client's plan can undergo substantial revisions. This would be particularly true during the time between the final two MET sessions.

Should the prepackaged discharge plan serve as the action plan of Motivational Enhancement Therapy? In each case, the MET therapist works with the client to answer this question. In the aftercare condition, the therapists help the clients evaluate prehospital problems, the feedback, and the hospital discharge plan to develop a unique action plan. This plan can include all or part of the prepackaged plan if the motivation elicited during the first sessions focuses on these elements. However, as clients consider their particular situation and address personal issues and situations, the MET action plan can be quite different from the prepackaged plan.

Disulfiram

Some clients will be discharged from the hospital on disulfiram, which must be taken regularly. There are several important considerations about disulfiram and ME therapy. Disulfiram can be a very helpful aid in promoting sobriety in clients who are impulsive and may need some built-in delays and deterrents to drinking. However, clients can see disulfiram as the sole cause of their sobriety. This can undermine self-motivation and self-efficacy. If clients are planning to use disulfiram as part of their postdischarge plans, it is *important to explore how the disulfiram will help* and *what role it will play in sobriety*. It is also helpful to elicit self-motivational statements that make clients the agents in the use of disulfiram. It is their decision to take disulfiram and their evaluation of the need for disulfiram that will help them to follow through with the prescription that makes disulfiram work. Ownership of the disulfiram plan and daily commitment to the prescription can certainly be a valuable part of the MET action plan and promote successful sobriety. Do not be afraid to include disulfiram in the plan, but only include it if the client endorses it and has a personal commitment to it. Often, disulfiram is the decision of the doctor and not the client. In this case, it is important not to undermine or sabotage the inpatient prescription but not to endorse or push it if the client does not demonstrate any commitment to the disulfiram. Focus your attention on other behaviors and ideas that can engage the client's interest and commitment.

Alcoholics Anonymous

It will be difficult, if not impossible, for any client to complete an inpatient stay without having a prescription to attend AA or to participate in the 12-Step recovery process. AA involvement is often a major element in the discharge plan prepared in the hospital and part of the hospital regimen. Thus, in the aftercare condition, it would be impossible to simply ignore AA involvement. However, because of the overlap with other treatment conditions, you need to be careful not to become an independent promoter of AA involvement. In the MET condition, it seems best to handle AA involvement the same as other aspects of the client's plan. Therapists do not originate or promote any one measure or method of achieving sobriety. Therapists do help clients to explore and evaluate both problems and solutions as indicated by the client or the feedback information.

Specifically, this approach would mean that AA involvement is examined if it is proposed by the client or has been a part of the client's experience. In this examination, the therapist explores the specifics, uses reflective listening, elicits motivational statements, and summarizes the client's plans and commitment with regard to AA involvement and 12-Step work. Some clients may simply be reflecting a party line, others may be convinced of the value of meetings, and still others may be committed to working with a sponsor and completing each of the 12 Steps of recovery. Understanding the client's level of understanding and commitment is the first step. If any level of AA involvement is included as an integral part of the action plan postdischarge, it needs to be monitored and examined as the therapist would do with any other method or measure decided by the client.

Motivational Enhancement Therapy attempts to identify motivations and maximize the client's commitment to a personal, individual plan of action. For clients who identify AA as a viable part of their plan, the task of MET is to enhance the personal motivation and commitment to follow through with that part of the plan. From this perspective, there is no conflict between AA involvement and MET. In fact, they can be quite compatible, particularly in the aftercare condition where the social support and philosophy of AA, if freely chosen by the client, can provide substantial assistance in achieving the goal of sobriety.

Feedback

Even after an inpatient stay, clients appear genuinely interested in the results and can gain information, insight, and motivation from the specific feedback given to them about their condition. Several cautions need to be heeded in giving feedback in the aftercare condition that may differ from the outpatient condition.

At times, the feedback on liver functioning and neuropsychological functioning will appear to be nonproblematic. This can be interpreted by a client as a sign that there are no problems or no damage. It is important to remember that the tests given provide only gross indicators and are not designed to assess subtle signs of damage or dysfunction. In other words, these tests do not give the client a clean bill of health and, if negative, need to be contrasted with the significance of the problem that needed hospital treatment. Having few indicators of damage can also be reframed to convey the message that the client is fortunate to not yet be showing gross symptoms. This message can be used to increase motivation for sobriety, since sobriety can ensure protection from any further alcohol-related damage.

Clients may be quite interested in having additional information and explanation of their physical condition. Since they are coming from a hospital setting, they may address the therapist as one who is well versed in medical conditions and problems. It is important for therapists to clarify specific issues, to acknowledge when they do not know an answer, and to obtain an answer for the next session or refer clients to the physician in charge of their case in the hospital. Issues of credibility and accuracy of information are important considerations in the feedback process.

Ambivalence and Attribution

ME therapists in aftercare settings should not be surprised to find ambivalence about drinking, and particularly about abstinence, among their clients. Many individuals who enter hospital treatment are motivated by external pressures or by current problems or concerns at the time of the hospitalization. The hospital stay can be a time of respite and even one of eroding motivation as the pressures or concerns recede. Therefore, it is critical not to assume motivation for sobriety postdischarge. Often, clients are motivated not to go back to the hospital, never to get to that prehospital state again, and not to have as many problems that drove them to drink. If you listen carefully, you will hear that these are not motivations about drinking but about the problems drinking caused.

In exploring the drinking problem, it is often helpful to get a clear understanding of what led to the prehospital pattern of drinking and the reason for hospitalization. It would be important to continue to connect psychosocial problems with drinking whenever this can clearly be done. Understanding how the postdischarge plan will address both drinking and other lifestyle, relationship, and employment issues can be a fruitful avenue of discussion. Listen carefully for what abstinence from drinking will mean for this client and what it will entail. Many of these clients have been living in alcohol-saturated environments. In fact, this may be part of the reason for hospitalization. Discharge from the protected setting of the hospital will severely test plans and ideas about abstinence. Even a firmly motivated stance during the first session in the hospital can be shaken to the foundations at the second session after the client is discharged. The first few weeks can be quite volatile with respect to motivations about sobriety and plans for using certain coping measures to ensure sobriety. Aftercare ME therapists need to be aware of these issues, probe for the ambivalence, and listen carefully to the client. Using reflective listening, supportive and empathic statements, and accurate, sensitive feedback will be particularly needed to handle the ambivalence of the aftercare client.

The hospital setting provides a safe environment for helping clients initiate an alcohol-free existence. The restricted setting, however, can have a deleterious effect on client attributions of success. Since access to alcohol cues is quite limited during detox and hospital stays, clients have to attribute some of their successful abstinence to external control. Part of the task of the aftercare ME therapist is to assist the client in retributing the success to internal causes. After all, the client chooses to enter and stay in the hospital and must choose the level of participation in the program as well as the level of commitment to sobriety. Thus, although it is true that the restricted setting is helpful, attribution to personal goals, effort, and achievement is important to increase self-efficacy. Since MET puts the responsibility for sobriety squarely on the client, it would be helpful to explore and assist in the attribution of success to the client rather than the hospital. This is an ongoing process that becomes more salient as the client is discharged and during the later sessions of MET.

Motivational Enhancement Therapy can be an effective aftercare treatment for clients discharged from various types of inpatient treatment. This aftercare approach can enhance the work accomplished by the clients during their inpatient program and can assist them in developing a solid plan for achieving and maintaining sobriety.

Appendix C: Therapist Selection, Training, and Supervision in Project MATCH

by Kathleen Carroll, Ph.D.

Specifications of treatment in manuals is intended to define and differentiate psychotherapies, to standardize therapist technique, and to permit replication by other investigators. However, it is essential that manual-guided therapies be implemented by qualified therapists who are trained to perform them effectively. Project MATCH uses extensive procedures to select, train, and monitor therapists in order to promote delivery of study treatments that are specific, discriminable, and delivered at a consistently high level of quality. These include (1) selection of experienced therapists committed to the type of therapy they would be performing, (2) extensive training to help therapists modify their repertoire to meet manual guidelines and to standardize performance across therapists and across sites, and (3) ongoing monitoring and supervision of each therapist's delivery of treatment during the main phase of the study to assure implementation of study treatments at a high and consistent level.

Therapist Selection

All MATCH therapist candidates are required to meet the following selection criteria: (1) completion of a master's degree or above in counseling, psychology, social work, or a closely related field (some exceptions to this requirement were made in individual cases), (2) at least 2 years of clinical experience after completion of degree or certification, (3) appropriate therapist technique, based on a videotaped example of a therapy session with an actual client submitted to the principal investigator at each site and to the Yale Coordinating Center, and (4) experience in conducting a type of treatment consistent with the MATCH treatment they would be conducting and experience treating alcoholics or a closely related clinical population.

These criteria are intended to facilitate (1) selection of appropriate therapists for the training program, as training is not intended to train novice therapists, but to familiarize experienced therapists with manual-guided therapy, and (2) implementation of MATCH treatments by experienced and credible therapists. For example, therapists selected for the Cognitive-Behavioral Coping Skills Therapy (CB) are experienced in cognitive and behavioral techniques; thus, the CB therapists are predominantly doctoral or masters-level psychologists. Therapists for the Twelve-Step Facilitation Program are predominantly individuals who have gone through 12-step recovery themselves, have been abstinent for several years, and are typically masters-level or certified alcoholism counselors. Therapists selected for the recently developed Motivation Enhancement Therapy (MET) have worked extensively with alcoholics and typically have experience in systems theory, family therapy, and motivational counseling.

Therapist Training

Training, supervision, and certification of therapists was centralized at the Yale Coordinating Center to facilitate consistency of treatment delivery across sites. Each therapist came to New Haven for a 3-day intensive training seminar, which included background and rationale for Project MATCH, extensive review of the treatment manual, review of taped examples of MATCH sessions, and practice exercises. Each therapist then returned to their clinical site and was assigned a minimum of two training cases, which were conducted following the MATCH protocol (e.g., weekly individual sessions, a maximum of two emergency and two conjoint sessions, truncated sessions for patients who arrived for a treatment session intoxicated).

All sessions from training cases were videotaped and sent to the Coordinating Center for review of the therapists' (1) adherence to manual guidelines, (2) level of skillfulness in treatment delivery, (3) appropriate structure and focus, (4) empathy and facilitation of the therapeutic alliance, and (5) nonverbal behavior. Yale Coordinating Center supervisors review all training sessions and provide weekly individual supervision to each therapist via telephone. Supplemental onsite supervision is delivered weekly by the project coordinator at each Clinical Research Unit.

Therapists were certified by the Yale Coordinating Center supervisors following successful completion of training cases. Therapists whose performance on initial cases was inadequate were assigned additional training cases until their performance improved. The average number of training cases was three, and therapists completed an average of 26 supervised sessions before certification.

Ongoing Monitoring

To monitor implementation of Project MATCH treatments, facilitate consistency of treatment quality and delivery across sites, and prevent therapist "drift" during the main phase of the study, all sessions are videotaped and sent to the Coordinating Center, where a proportion of each subject's sessions (one-third of all sessions for Cognitive-Behavioral and Twelve-Step Facilitation, one half of all MET sessions) are reviewed by the supervisors. Telephone supervision is provided on a monthly basis by the Coordinating Center supervisors and supplemented with weekly onsite group supervision at each Clinical Research Unit.

All sessions viewed are rated for therapist skillfulness, adherence to manual guidelines, and delivery of manual-specified active ingredients unique to each approach. These ratings are sent monthly to the project coordinators at each site to alert local supervisors to therapist drift. Therapists whose performance deviates in quality or adherence to the manual are "redlined" by the Coordinating Center, and the frequency of sessions monitored and supervision is increased until the therapist's performance returns to acceptable levels.

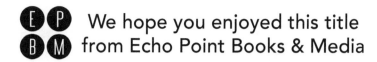

CPSIA information can be obtained
at www.ICGtesting.com
Printed in the USA
BVHW011557221022
649804BV00003B/17

9 781626 548572